SCIENCE NEWS
VII

Science
News
VII

PENGUIN BOOKS

1948

First published May, 1948

Photogravure plates printed by
Eric Bemrose Ltd., Liverpool

Made and printed in Great Britain
for Penguin Books Ltd., Harmondsworth, Middlesex
by C. Nicholls & Company Limited
London Manchester Reading

CONTENTS

Photographic supplement between pages 64 and 65

Editorial

CURIOUSLY enough, although nobody talks of 1939-45 as the war which ended War, nobody is yet discussing the form the next armed conflict will take. The exciting and terrible power of the atom bomb seems to have hypnotised us into claiming that the next war will end civilisation, and therefore must not occur; and at the same time that we will defend our way of life against anyone who tries to thrust another way upon us. It may not be of Britain's choosing; it may not be about or against Germany; but sooner or later, such being the way of mankind, it is highly probable another war will break out and we shall all be involved. It seems worth while to face this future realistically, which diminishes the terror. What will it be like?

Bacteriological warfare, at present a top secret on all sides, is a weapon aimed at the whole population. It seems possible that it might be developed along two lines. One is the simple spreading of infectious disease, for instance, by dropping large numbers of plague-infected rats into a city to start an epidemic, or by spraying infantile paralysis virus into the air over a town in a special way to ensure its aerial persistence and consequent continued infectivity. Although it is true that perhaps only two persons in every hundred exposed would get the disease seriously, or even at all, yet in a city of 500,000 this means 10,000 cases, which are quite enough to swamp all normal medical services and result in the stoppage of all activity, and a cease-fire. The other mode of attack depends on the fact that some bacteria produce amazingly powerful poisons. The toxin of botulism, for instance, is deadly even in the merest traces. It would be possible to make it pure by the pound and distribute it in water supplies or by aerial sprays with devastating effect.

Clearly the reply to this kind of warfare rests with the medical services. They will develop ways of rendering poisons harmless and the air fit to breathe, and they will teach everybody the rudiments of nursing and the recognition of the infectious diseases.

As for the atom bomb, apart from its use as a surprise opening to a war, which could probably thus be prematurely terminated through the resulting panic, its fearsomeness may be over-rated. It produces three kinds of attack: the destructive shock wave (blast), fires (flash) and radiation sickness. The first two of these can be minimised by a proper system of dispersal, deep shelters, and the increased use of underground food stores and factories, as already worked to some extent in 1939-45. Radiation sickness, its prevention, its treatment, is again a problem for the medical services. In fact the next war will be *par excellence* a medical war. Its outcome will depend entirely on the progress of medical research and the training of the Civil Defence Services.

These are a few random speculations: every scientist has his own pet ideas of what to expect and how to deal with it. The actual progress of military research can obviously not be included in *Science News*, but it seems worth while to draw attention to the kind of planning and development that must be going on. It is no use putting one's head under the blankets, and in an issue devoted largely to the applied sciences (High-Speed Flight, Craftsmanship, the uses of Photography, Calculating Machines) it would be wrong not to include at least some reference to the most important applications of all—to the next War.

Measuring Craftsmanship

DR G. W. SCOTT BLAIR

IT all looked so easy – until I tried it myself! Under the potter's hands the mass of clay climbed up so gracefully and evenly until the bowl was formed. I knew, of course, that the clay must be plastic enough to hold together and not to crumble in its rapid deformations, yet firm enough to hold its height. I asked the potter how he could tell whether a new batch of clay had the right 'plasticity'. 'Well', he said, twisting a rod of moist clay round in his hands, 'you can see if it'll stand bending like this; but really, when you've been making pots for thirty years as I have, you'll know the feel of your clay all right.' 'But how do you teach the youngsters?' I asked. 'Well, I can't rightly say that I do teach them. They learn for themselves, there's no short cut to knowing your clay!'

I tried my friend the baker. He was just starting to knead up his dough. 'That's a better flour' he said; 'That'll take about 15 gallons a sack!' 'How do you tell how much water it'll take?' 'Well – when you've been on this job for as long as I have ...'

So I went to the cheese store – rows of shelves from floor to ceiling almost as far as the eye could reach – literally thousands of cheeses. 'I wish my thumb didn't tire so quickly!' said the grader, jabbing that organ into the top of one of the cheeses. 'Ah, that's a better body for you!' I gathered that this remark referred to some quality of the cheese and not to the fallible human instrument used to test it. The grader was an old man and I wondered how many years it had taken him to learn his very skilled trade.

Now I've been more than twenty years at my job – a research physicist. I hope perhaps that with the large card

9

index I've collected and the much less reliable filing system of my memory, I'm more use at the job than I was when I started as a youngster with no more mental and physical equipment than my hastily acquired examination knowledge and my set of students' text books.

But this is the point: – If I had measured the viscosity of an oil or the electrical resistance of a wire even in those days, I should have got the same result as my most learned professor; or, if I hadn't, he would easily have spotted some silly mistake in my measurement. It would have been unthinkable for him to have said to me: 'When you've been doing physical measurements for twenty years or so you'll get a different answer.'

How does the viscosity of an oil or the resistance of a wire differ from the plasticity of a clay or the body of a cheese?

It would not be true to say that these latter things can't be measured by instruments – to some extent they can; but, unlike viscosity and electrical resistance, the best we can hope from measurements of plasticity and body is that they shall not depend on the skill of the person who makes the test (once he has acquired the very simple technique needed to work the apparatus). The results will depend on the exact design of the machine and precise technique for its use; nor can we be perfectly sure that the 'plasticity' or 'body' that is measured will be exactly what the potter or the baker means by these terms.

Unfortunately, in most industries, the 'properties' of materials that are of practical importance are not simple physical properties like viscosity, or electrical resistance, but complex concepts like plasticity, of which Brogniart said, over a hundred years ago, 'On a souvent parlé de cette propriété, on semble la connaître, mais on n'en a qu'une vague idée'.

This being so, industry is bound to tend to rely on the skill of the old craftsman who knows his materials – nor is it always desirable to replace such craftsmen by machines. But there are many cases, especially in these times of economic difficulty, when the necessarily large scale of modern production makes it essential to control materials and processes by less subjective methods.

Cheese used to be made on the farm with a few gallons of milk at a time, and I am quite certain that no one will make anything as good as the best English farmhouse cheese, without craftsmanship, by means of clocks and machines. Yet it is positively pathetic to see an elderly and obviously harrassed cheese-maker trying to cope with a batch of 'slow starter' or an unexpected deterioration in milk quality in a big modern factory handling some 20,000 gallons of milk a day.

A director of an old-established firm said to me recently, 'We're prepared to use Science when it helps but not when it makes things worse'. I think that by 'Science' he meant 'Mechanisation' or 'Instrumentation', as the Americans call the mechanisation of testing materials. Science, as organised common experience properly applied, could hardly make things worse. But I sympathised with him, for I well remember on the continent some years before the war a country where the progress of vitally important wheat breeding experiments was controlled solely on the results from a dough quality testing machine, which I was able to show from figures already available on the spot, bore no relation whatever to the quality of the doughs as judged by experienced bakers and millers.

It therefore seems necessary to 'measure' craftsmanship in order to find out just what these 'properties' are which the potter, the baker or the cheese-maker claim to be able to assess by handling materials; to find out how small a change in such 'properties' the expert can correctly detect; by how much his judgments on any given material will differ on different occasions; how far the judgments of one expert differ from those of another; whether there is any quicker way of teaching this craft to apprentices; and whether when the hands serve as a testing machine, the expert uses his joints and muscles to their best advantage.

Often the expert does not himself know to what extent his judgments depend on sight or feel. Thus Binns found that a highly skilled wool-top tester could judge the softness of a wool no better than could a school-child when both were blindfolded, though the experts were certain that judgments were made by feel and not by sight. The baker, too, uses his eyes in judging the quality of doughs. Katz, following experiments on blindfolded bakers, reports that 'the baker, in judging doughs, is not absolutely lost without vision, but on the other hand, he can make the optical impressions the only ones to rely on if we want him to do so'. Katz himself kneaded the dough and asked the baker to judge its quality purely by sight.

Stickiness is an important factor in judging dough quality and must be taken into account in designing any instrument intended to measure 'body'. In the judging of stickiness, Katz found that temperature plays an unexpected part. 'The higher the temperature, the less sticky a dough will feel, the lower the temperature the greater the apparent (not the real) stickiness.'

Miss Sullivan has shown how misleading the feel of materials on the fingers can be if sight is excluded. A subject's finger was dipped into water at a series of different temperatures, the hand being screened so that the nature of the liquid could not be seen. As the temperature rose from the freezing point to 42°C., the feel was described progressively as (1) mushy – like partly-melted snow; (2) muddy – like mercury; (3) gelatinous – like gelatine; (4) wet – like water; (5) (at blood heat) oily – like oil; (6) greasy – like melted butter.

V. G. W. Harrison, in his interesting book on *The Definition and Measurement of Gloss** tells of the very complex blending of factors by which the gloss of paper is judged. 'Gloss meters' of all kinds have been made by the physicist, but Harrison says 'To sum up: for metals, paints

* Printing and Allied Trades Research Association, London, December 1945.

and varnishes, the "objective" gloss meter may be satisfactory for certain purposes; for textiles and papers, no'.

In our work at the National Institute for Research in Dairying, we have found that expert cheese-makers tend to judge quality of cheese as a whole and that such judgments of quality are more reproducible than are those of non-experts. But the experts find it hard to judge one factor (say firmness) separately from another (such as springiness) and, as a result of this, the judgments of non-experts, though less self-consistent, often agree better than do those of the experts with testing instruments which measure isolated physical properties.

Plate 38 shows a cheese-maker testing the quality of cheese curd in the making. Plate 39 shows an instrument for measuring the weight and height (and hence the density) of a cylinder of curd on the principle that the softer the curd, the less easily can the heavier whey drain out of the test-cylinder to be replaced by lighter air. The results of the density test agree well with the expert's judgment.

Plate 40 shows a grader about to judge the firmness or body of a 'plug' taken with a special borer from the cheese. Plate 41 shows a hardness tester in which the penetration of a ball into the surface of the cheese under a standard load is measured. This serves as a kind of 'mechanical thumb' and agrees fairly well with the grader's opinions. Keestra, in Holland, has made a similar study of the firmness of butter as judged by 'thumbing'.

In order to determine the 'thresholds' or just noticeable differences (j.n.d.'s) when people compare the firmness of two materials by squeezing one in each hand, we started by making experiments on materials which are physically simpler than cheese. Firmness of cheese cannot be expressed by any one single 'physical property', but there are certain bitumens which, though of about the same firmness as cheese, have the property of flowing at a perfectly steady rate under constant pressure and, when pressure is varied, at a rate proportional to it, so that even at the smallest pressures they will flow very slowly. This means that for these materials, the conception of firmness must depend simply* on the constant ratio of pressure to rate of flow, which is called viscosity. Viscosity can be measured in a variety of ways, all of which should give the same answer if the temperature doesn't change.

Though rubber is not perfectly elastic, as a first approximation it is true to say that just as bitumen flows twice as *fast* when you press twice as hard, so rubber deforms twice as *far* and stays put when the pressure is constant. For rubber, firmness therefore depends on the nearly constant ratio of pressure to amount of deformation, which is called an 'elastic modulus'. When people were asked to squeeze, one in each hand, small cylinders of bitumen and, on other occasions, small cylinders of rubber and to compare them for firmness, trying to exert a steady pressure on each occasion, it is not perhaps surprising that it was found that rubbers could be compared with one another with about three times as small a j.n.d. as that found for bitumens. The former could be compared statically, by comparing amounts of deformation; the latter were flowing all the time and had to be judged by rate of flow.

Skilled cheese-makers did not notice smaller differences than the rest of us, but younger and less educated people did rather better than older and better educated people. I remembered this when, on a recent visit to a pottery, I watched very young girls manipulating clay with great skill and was told how satisfactory many of them were.

The j.n.d.'s don't seem to depend on the sensitivity of the skin so much as on the frame of mind of the tester. Routine analysts, who are used to doing very careful work day by day without knowing the purpose of the tests, and who do not worry as to whether they are doing better than their neighbours, showed strikingly low j.n.d.'s. Expert handlers of materials – cheese-makers, bakers, etc. – are apt to be

* Certain precautions have to be taken to ensure that this is really true.

suspicious in tests of this kind – and suspicion has a devastating effect on the thresholds.

It might seem therefore that such experiments do not tell
us much about the real skill of the craftsman. Nor do they
unless we go further to study more complex situations.

What happens if you compare for firmness a bitumen in
one hand with a rubber in the other? The physicist will tell
you with horror that you can no more describe a viscosity
as greater or less than an elastic modulus than you can call
20 seconds greater or less than 15 feet. This, in a sense, is
true. Yet few people have any difficulty in comparing rubber
and bitumen for firmness. The decision as to which is the
firmer depends on the time allowed for the squeezing. If
this is controlled by means of a metronome or similar device,
it is found that the time of squeezing and the elastic modulus
of the rubber are equally important in effecting the decision.

By what factor is the judgment made? In comparisons of
rubber with rubber, the deciding factor is the distances
through which the rubbers compress under the steady
pressure exerted.* In comparing bitumen with bitumen, it
is presumably the rates of flow which are compared. In
comparing a rubber with a bitumen, the judgment can hardly
depend on a rate, since, except during the first fraction of a
second during which the pressure is being applied, the rubber
'stays put'; nor in fact is the amount of deformation in the
course of the squeezing the deciding factor. If the amount of
deformation were the criterion, we should expect that a
rubber would be equated in firmness to a bitumen if the
elastic modulus of the rubber were numerically equal to the
viscosity of the bitumen, in cases where the time allowed for
squeezing was one second. This would follow from the fact
that the elastic modulus is defined as the ratio of pressure
to *amount* of deformation and the viscosity as its ratio to
rate of deformation which, for a constant pressure, is given
by the amount of flow in one second.

* Proper precautions are, of course, taken to allow for right and
left-handedness.

In fact, it is found that only a third of a second's squeezing would be needed to give, on the average of many tests, an 'equal firmness' judgment between such samples.

It is concluded that the entity by which firmness is judged in such cases is neither a distance nor a rate but something in between. In comparing complex cheese-like materials with standard rubber cylinders the same thing happens, only here time is not as important as is consistency – for cheese itself it is about a fifth as important. This relative importance of time – one fifth in this case – has been called the 'Dissipation Coefficient'.

The dissipation coefficient of a cheese-like material can be calculated, then, from the massed results of a large number of squeezing tests in which the material is compared with standard rubbers or bitumens by enough people to eliminate the personal factor. But it can also be measured by compressing cylinders of the material under constant pressure on a machine. As the cylinder compresses, it increases in area and the force has to be correspondingly increased so that the pressure, which is the force on each square centimetre of surface, can remain constant.

The values of the dissipation coefficients agree excellently when measured by these two quite different methods, which means that out of all the complexities of 'firmness' we have evidently found something to satisfy the physicist which is independent not only of the observer but of the method of measurement.

What are these peculiar entities which lie, as it were, between distances and velocities, by which firmness is judged? Their mathematics had been worked out many years ago by Heaviside (now of radio fame), but their introduction into problems of measuring craftsmanship is entirely new.

It has been suggested that they are needed in this field for rather an interesting reason. For all practical and scientific purposes we tell the time by a clock. We say that two minutes are of equal length because the hand of the clock moves over equal distances on the dial in those times. But clocks don't all tell exactly the same time. Even the rotations of the earth are very gradually slowing down. When we say 'slowing down', we must mean getting slower in relation to something else. The final criterion of equality of intervals of time is that light, out in open space, takes equal times to traverse equal distances, whose equality could be measured, in theory at least, by means of a foot rule. On this definition depends our concept of constant velocity and, in simple physical processes, the properties which are found to be constant, like the viscosity of our bitumen, are built up from velocities defined in this way.

But in more complex materials like cheese, clay or dough, the natural time scale is not dependent on rays of light, the rotations of the earth or the laboratory clock. Still less does the craftsman or anyone else handling the materials have a Newtonian clock (as it is called) in his brain. Quite other time scales are used and, if we insist on translating the results into terms of seconds and minutes (as we very rightly do), we must expect that our constant 'properties' of materials, or 'quasi-properties', as I prefer to call them, will be found to be built up of units which are not exactly distances, velocities or accelerations, but lie between these entities.

The relationships between these new ideas and some of the concepts of Relativity, which also modifies Newtonian physics, are interesting.

In conclusion, I would say that I believe this to be the sort of way in which Science can best fulfil its function. From the potter at his wheel to the philosopher at his desk stretches one single line of investigation. 'Pure Science' is a misnomer, since it implies that some science is impure. Science in the workshop without its counterpart in the study is equally meaningless. Measuring craftsmanship would seem quite effectively to illustrate the unity of scientific advance.

The Hearing of Insects

DR GABRIELE RABEL

PHYSIOLOGISTS who, guided by an understandable preju-
dice, searched for ears on the heads of insects, did not find
any. But, unexpectedly, ear-like organs have been found in
insects at odd places. How do these compare with our human
ears?

Essential for our sense of hearing are two structures:
(1) the drum (tympanum), a delicate, tightly-stretched membrane with a cavity behind it, (2) a long, spirally-coiled tube
(the cochlea) which contains, attached to it along one edge,
an extremely delicate ribbon, likewise spirally coiled, made
up of about 24,000 elastic fibres which gradually decrease
in length. These fibres are supposed to act like the strings
of a piano, each responding to a certain tone, the longer
fibres vibrating to the lower notes. This much quoted
interpretation was propounded eighty years ago by Helm-
holtz, but, surprisingly, it has still the scientific status of a
'very plausible hypothesis'.

Now there are a few groups of insects which also have a
tympanic membrane on either side of their body, with air-
sacs behind. Grasshoppers, locusts, cicadas and certain
moths carry them on their first abdominal segment, other
moths on their thorax, while crickets, and according to some
writers, termites, have their ears on the knees of their fore-
legs. Roughly, one can say that those insects which make
music (as distinct from mere noise) have also an organ to
receive it.

But have they anything to fulfil the sound-analysing
function of the cochlear ribbon? Scientists formerly believed
they had. For one finds in all insects structures which con-
sist of parallel elements – elongated spindle-shaped sensory

18

cells whose axes are prolonged into nerve fibres on the central side while on the other side they are in contact with the so-called 'scolopales' (pointed stakes). On the theory that the elongated parallel elements act as chords (strings) and have a 'tonus' or tension like strings, these structures have been given the name 'chordotonal organs', but they occur in all insects whether provided with a tympanum or not and they are no longer regarded as resonators. Yet some of them are associated with hearing and Eggers maintains that one can catch tympanal organs in the act of developing from chordotonal ones. Certain hairs and other body appendages are receptors for low frequencies transmitted through the substrate. Caterpillars and other larvæ have them too. And there is in a scientific paper a tale of larvæ who were directed in their motions by the chirps of their parents.

That some insects genuinely hear is no longer contested. Leydig observed drummers training on the Würzburg parade ground uproariously supported by a cicada chorus in the vineyards which stopped when the drummers stopped and started again when they did. The entomologist Collenette was present at a 'conversation' between a bird and a butterfly, their clicks being quite similar in quality and speed. 'The prompt response of the insect left no doubt that it was replying to the bird.' Musical conversations between two male insect songsters in which they go on for hours alternating rhythmically in their notes are often described, and a much admired feature in insects is their singing in concert. One of the singers may drop out for a while, but when he resumes the musical play, he is always in perfect synchronism with his fellows.

There have been endless controversies as to whether females are attracted to males by sound or rather by sight or smell or vibrations transmitted by the substrate, until by his most ingenious experiments with crickets, Johann Regen of Vienna disposed of all alternatives.

When he put a chirping but invisible male in competition

with a visible but silent one, the visible was unhesitatingly by-passed, even if the chirp came from a distant room over the phone. When he switched the current off, the female turned away. When he switched it on, she came, even if it meant fighting her way over a mountain of 150 cm. or through high grass.

Experiments with artificial imitation of insect song showed that male crickets and grasshoppers can be cheated only when they are new and quite inexperienced. When they grow older, they immediately stop their duets if a bogus male takes the place of a real one and tries to chime in in the same rhythm.

But how do insects discriminate between tone qualities if they have no sound analysing device such as mammals possess? Trying to answer this question, Dr Pumphrey, of Cambridge, broke new ground. His answer is: Amplitude Modulation.

Just as bats have applied the ultrasonic echo method since time immemorial, insects have operated with amplitude modulation long before engineers had any idea of its existence. Amplitude modulation comes about when an oscillation of constant frequency is interfered with by another, perhaps irregular oscillation so that owing to this interference the amplitude varies. In the wireless, a high constant frequency is produced by an electric oscillating circuit, a low one by music or speech. What can be the analogy in insects?

Grasshoppers or locusts produce their sounds by drawing a toothed ridge called a scraper across the sharp edge of a wing. Pumphrey thinks that the constant high frequency is given by the natural frequency of the wing, incited to its vibrations by the scraper, while the teeth of it provide the modulation. Not much work has yet been done to determine the frequency of each component. Pumphrey's evidence is indirect

If a mammalian cochlea fitted with suitable electrodes is exposed to well-defined sound vibrations, it gives an electrical response corresponding in frequency to the sound presented to it. But if an insect tympanum is thus examined, a pure tone, even in the range of its maximum sensitivity (5-20 kc. p.s.) produces a random electrical response which is the same for all frequencies presented and shows no time pattern (rhythm) at all.

When, however, a pure tone of 8,000 cycles p.s. was combined with a vibration of under 300 c.p.s., the nervous discharge consisted of bursts of activity which corresponded to the lower frequency. There is a striking contrast between the behaviour of a human and a locust ear in this case, though they are both equally sensitive to 8,000 cycles. If the pure high tone is combined with a low-pitched one, man hears a trill. But he notices little change if the lower frequency is widely varied, while he is sensitive to very slight variations in the high frequency. The contrary is true for the locust, according to the observed electrical responses. And this would imply that the insect can readily distinguish different modes of using the scraper while it is indifferent to the natural frequencies of wings.

It is a fact that sounds which seem identical to a human ear, can be easily distinguished by an insect and vice versa. In Regen's experiments, a virgin female cricket would approach a telephone even if the chirp appeared unrecognisably distorted to a human observer.

There is a theory that some classes of animals, including man, have auditory organs which respond to the pressure changes brought about by sound waves, but not to displacement changes, while for other classes, including insects, the contrary is true. In the case of those insects which have tympanic organs, the view that what they perceive is displacement not pressure is confirmed by the fact that these organs are capable of discerning the direction from which the sound comes. In the case of ants, which have no tympanic organs, Autrum confirmed this theory by a very original method. Sound was directed vertically downward upon a reflecting surface, thereby setting up standing waves. Ants which walked on the reflecting surface were in a region of maximum pressure and minimum displacement, and such ants did not respond at all to sound. But at a quarter wave length from the wall is a region of maximum displacement and minimum pressure. When Autrum lifted his ant cylinder which had a wire net at its bottom, into one of the regions of maximum displacement, he noticed a strong reaction to the sound, a sudden anxiety, fearful running about, and continued restlessness.

Autrum also examined the sensitivity of longhorn grass-hoppers to ultrasonics and found that their tympanal organ responded to frequencies up to 90 kc. p.s., even at very low intensity.

Approaching
the Speed of Sound

PROFESSOR O. G. SUTTON

HITHERTO the behaviour of bodies moving at very high speeds through the air has been mainly the concern of the ballistician, but with the successful development of jet propulsion it is now possible to contemplate aircraft sufficiently powerful to be capable of reaching and even surpassing the speed of sound (about 760 miles per hour at normal temperatures). Speeds of this order are low for modern artillery whose projectiles travel steadily and attain high accuracy in their flight, and at first sight it is not obvious why it is difficult to reach the speed of sound in a piloted aircraft.

To understand completely what is involved in 'getting through the speed of sound' demands a knowledge of the complex and largely mathematical science of aerodynamics. It is possible, however, to describe in fairly general terms some of the difficulties involved, and the subject can be clarified by the use of a simple analogy which, is, in fact, more exact than might appear at first.

To begin with, the motion of an aircraft wing or other supporting surface creates a force due to the resistance of the air, and as long ago as 1809 Sir George Cayley, one of the pioneer English workers in this field, accurately described the problem of mechanical flight as that of 'making a surface support a weight by the application of power to the resistance of the air'. In aerodynamics it is customary to resolve the reaction of the air on a surface into two components, namely *lift*, which is that part of the force acting upwards at right angles to the surface, and is thus desirable, and *drag*, which is the component at right angles to the lift and which constitutes a loss since it resists the forward

23

motion of the surface through the air. An *aerofoil,* such as a wing or tail fin, is simply a surface of special shape which on being propelled through the air produces in certain conditions considerably more lift than drag. The problem of high speed flight is largely that of producing an assembly of such surfaces which can be relied upon to maintain a high lift/drag ratio and to remain stable in the exacting conditions met with as the speed approaches that of sound.

Drag

We commence by considering how drag, which represents energy wasted, changes with increasing speed. This is most simply done by comparison with the cooling of a hot body. Such a body loses heat (i.e. energy) in three ways – by conduction, convection and radiation. In the same way a body moving through air loses energy by *skin friction* (analogous to conduction), *eddy formation* (analogous to convection) and *wave formation* (analogous to radiation).

Skin Friction

Heat is conducted from a body by the molecules of air coming into contact with the hot surface and acquiring additional energy of vibration which is manifested as a rise of temperature in the layers of air near the surface. In the same way molecules of air adhere to the surface of a moving body and thus acquire from it energy of motion. This effect is called *viscosity* and acts in a very thin layer enveloping the body – the so-called *boundary-layer* of modern aerodynamics. This type of resistance occurs with all moving bodies and can only be reduced by making the exposed surface very smooth.

Eddy Formation

When a body with a sharply truncated tail (such as a shell) moves through the atmosphere at a moderate speed it is observed that the air flows smoothly around it until the tail is reached. At this point the stream is unable to make the sharp turn required to get round the corner and the flow separates, forming a well-defined *wake*. In the wake masses of air coil themselves up into vortices or eddies, detach themselves from the body and drift away downstream. This is analogous to what happens with convection from a hot body when masses of warm air rise bodily from the surface and carry away heat to other regions. In the case of the moving body there are of course no corresponding differences in density, but the swirling eddies left behind in the wake have robbed the moving body of some of its energy to feed their own motion, and this is felt as an increased resistance, known as *form drag*.

If the tail is carefully tapered it is possible to prevent violent separation and so to avoid most of this loss, and bodies designed in this way are called *streamlined*. A streamlined body is, in fact, simply a body whose form drag is small compared with its skin friction – in other words, a body which leaves behind it only a small wake. At these speeds the importance to be attached to skin friction thus depends on the magnitude of the form drag; in a modern aircraft, for example, form drag is so small that it is worth while taking pains to get a smooth surface everywhere, but a high polish on the body of a car is a matter of pride to the owner and no more.

Wave Formation

The two types of resistance described above make up the entire drag* at speeds which are well below that of sound, and at these speeds the shape of the tail is more important than that of the head in designing a body of low resistance. As the speed of the body approaches that of sound, however, an entirely new phenomenon appears, which is akin to radiation in that it involves wave motion. Radiation from a hot body is usually unimportant at low temperatures, and similarly wave formation by a moving body does not really

---

* For an aerofoil it is necessary to introduce also the *induced drag*, i.e. the part of the total resistance which depends entirely on the lift.

begin to become important until the velocity is at least two-thirds that of sound (about 500 miles per hour at normal temperatures).

It is not at first obvious why the speed of sound should enter, but the reason becomes clearer when it is realised that at low speeds the air meeting the nose of the body is not appreciably compressed and made more dense but is deflected aside, something like a good-natured crowd giving way to a slowly moving car. At higher speeds the air near the body has, crudely speaking, no chance to get out of the way and is compressed. When such sudden compression takes place the air near the body responds by passing on the blow and the disturbance is propagated throughout the fluid as a *wave*, consisting of a succession of condensations and rarefactions. If the disturbance is small the result is an ordinary sound wave, but if the blow is severe, such as occurs with a massive body rushing rapidly through the air or with an explosion, the result is a definite atmospheric discontinuity called a *shock wave* which travels initially with a speed somewhat greater than that of sound. As it moves, the shock wave continuously loses energy and slows down, ultimately degenerating into an ordinary sound wave.

Thus in the case of an aircraft or a projectile moving at a speed just below that of sound the air at the nose is compressed and a spherical wave front rushes ahead, the whole disturbance growing like a soap bubble. With increasing speed the body approaches nearer and nearer to the wave front until ultimately it catches it up and thereafter the wave remains attached to the nose and is carried along with it, forming a well-defined cone with its apex at the nose. These wave fronts are extremely sharp – it can be shown mathematically that the region of highly-compressed air is usually not more than a small fraction of an inch in thickness – and they therefore photograph well (see plate 45) and even (as happened during the bombardment of London by V-weapons) have been seen, by favourably-placed observers, as a thin curved line rising from the scene of a distant explosion.

Compressibility

Phenomena of this sort are said to be due to *compressibility* and give rise to what is known in ballistics as 'head resistance' and in aerodynamics as *wave drag*. Because of their importance in gunnery the effects of such wave formation on resistance are now well established. In the narrow zone of speed known as the *transonic region* (between about 600 and 800 miles per hour at normal temperatures) the resistance changes extremely rapidly with velocity, suddenly shooting up to a high value and then, rather more slowly, steadying down to a more gradual rate of increase as the speed becomes highly supersonic. This sudden jump in resistance indicates the extra energy used in compressing and setting in motion the air to form the system of shock waves at the nose and other parts of the body. At these high speeds the shape of the head becomes of considerable importance and with a high velocity shell most of the energy lost in overcoming air resistance is 'radiated' away in shock waves. This is in sharp contrast to what happens at lower speeds when the main loss of energy is associated with the formation of eddies in the wake. Figure 1 shows diagrammatically these various sources of loss.

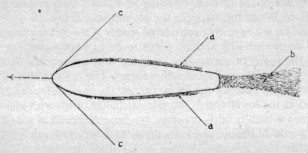

Figure 1—Sources of resistance on a moving body:
(a) boundary layer (skin friction);
(b) wake (eddy formation);
(c) shock waves (wave resistance).
Shock waves may also form at other points on the body.

The Mechanism of Lift

We now consider the other – and useful – part of the reaction of the air, namely the lift force which actually causes
an aircraft to fly. At subsonic speeds lift can now be said to
be well understood, thanks chiefly to the pioneer work of
F. W. Lanchester in the early years of this century. Like
form drag it is connected with rotary motion or circulation
in the air, but now in a well ordered form.

When an aircraft takes off, its aerofoil supporting surfaces
start moving through the air at a small angle to the horizontal, and almost the first thing that happens is that each
wing sheds an eddy (called the 'starting vortex') at the rear
edge. The reaction to this vortex causes circulation around
the aerofoil with the result that the air moves more rapidly
over the upper cambered side than over the lower flat side.
By Bernoulli's theorem this causes decreased pressure on
the upper surface and increased pressure on the lower
surface, so that the wings are both 'sucked' and 'pushed'
upwards, thus giving the necessary force to make the heavy
machine rise. As the angle of incidence increases, the lift
also increases and the aircraft is able to climb, but if the
tilt is made too large the flow on the upper surface separates
and eddies are formed, resulting in a sharp drop in lifting
power. When this happens the aircraft is said to *stall*.

So far we have only considered speeds at which the effects
of compressibility are too small to be of importance, but
as the speed of the air-flow over the wing approaches that
of sound a new phenomenon appears. The pilot is able to
increase or decrease the lift by altering the angle of incidence
and at the lower speeds the rate of change of lift with incidence is usually fairly constant, but near the speed of sound
this rate of change suddenly drops to a very low value together with a large decrease in lift itself. In this critical
region of speed the pilot is thus faced not only with a rapid
rise in resistance but also with a sudden loss of lift and
control, a phenomenon known as *shock stall*. There are also
other disturbing effects, making it difficult for the aircraft

to remain on an even keel (chiefly due to the fact that flow conditions are not exactly the same over the wings and tail planes) so that, taken altogether, the dangers of high speed flight are not difficult to imagine.

The Mach Number

At this point it becomes necessary to introduce a concept of major importance in the dynamics of high-speed flow. It can be shown by fairly simple considerations that all phenomena at high speeds depend not on the absolute velocity of the body but on the so-called *Mach number* which is the ratio of the air speed to the velocity of sound. (That is, a Mach number less than unity indicates a subsonic speed and one greater than unity, supersonic speed. The transonic region covers, very roughly, the range of Mach numbers between about 0.75 and 1.1). Since the velocity of sound changes quite considerably with air temperature, the Mach number depends not only on the aircraft speed but also on the height, the season and the locality of the flight.

The phenomenon which we have been discussing first appears at a certain Mach number known as the *critical Mach number* whose exact value depends upon a number of factors. There is also some evidence that if the speed is high enough matters become easier again, so that there may be an upper as well as a lower critical Mach number, or in other words, safety lies in keeping well away from the transonic region of speed.

The Design of High-Speed Aircraft

It is an unfortunate fact for the understanding of high speed flight that not only is the mathematical theory of fluid motion at these velocities extremely difficult and only partially developed, but also that phenomena at high velocities are often quite contrary to what experience at every-day speeds would lead one to expect. (One of the most striking examples of this is that whereas at low speeds, as we have seen, a fluid cannot easily turn a sharp corner without the flow separating and forming eddies, at supersonic speeds there are apparently no such difficulties and the fluid is able to get around quite smoothly). If however, certain facts of compressible flow theory are accepted it is possible to explain in a short space some, at least, of the factors which influence the design of high-speed aircraft.

To attain very high velocities in a practicable aircraft it is obvious that wave drag must be reduced to a minimum. At low speeds the drag of a wing is not greatly affected by its thickness (up to a limit) but the wave drag of a wing moving at high speeds is proportional to the square of the thickness plus a term proportional to the square of the lift. This means that supersonic aircraft should have thin low lift wings, requirements that conflict with other demands for great structural strength and considerable weight-carrying power.

The necessity of keeping the flow over the wings below the critical Mach number has meant a considerable change in the shape of aircraft. As we have seen, the lift/drag ratio collapses very rapidly once the Mach number M reaches the critical value (say $M = 0.75$). In its simplest form the mathematical theory indicates that the velocity which matters in calculating the effective Mach number for the wing is the component of the speed perpendicular to the leading edge. With straight wings, this velocity is obviously the same as the forward speed of the aircraft, but if the wings are given a certain amount of *sweepback* (Fig. 2), the velocity perpendicular to the leading edge will be only a fraction of the forward velocity. On this simple theory, as indicated by Busemann in 1935, if M_o is the Mach number for the aircraft as a whole, the effective Mach number for the wing will be $M_o cos\theta$, where θ is the angle of sweepback. This means that M_o itself may be above the critical value with the effective Mach number for the wing still safely below the critical, or in other words, the use of swept-back wings raises the critical Mach number for the aircraft and allows the higher speeds to be reached without the danger of shock stall.

The more exact theory shows that the advantage is not

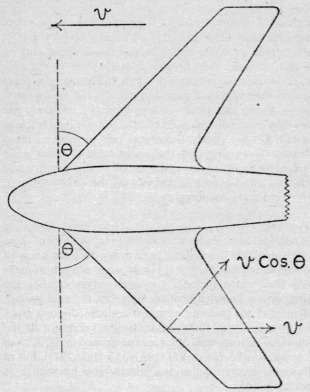

Figure 2—Aircraft with sweptback wings.

$v =$ velocity of the aircraft forwards, or of the air flow over it in the opposite direction.

$v \cos \theta =$ velocity of air flow perpendicular to the leading edge of the wings.

quite as great as indicated by the simple cosine law given above, and there are also certain compensating disadvantages introduced by sweepback, but the net effect is undoubtedly beneficial. There are also other variants of the idea, notably the 'delta' or triangular wing, but the discussion of these is beyond the scope of the present article.

Conclusions

Prophecy in scientific matters is perhaps only slightly less hazardous than in other fields of human activity, but it seems highly probable that safe supersonic flight will be attained and may even become commonplace in the next decade or two. Simultaneously, it is likely that designers will turn their attention more and more to the 'flying wing' type of aircraft (see plates 44 and 46) and a relatively few years may see the disappearance of the conventional fuselage and tail. On the purely theoretical side progress is more difficult to foreshadow, but the considerable advances made in recent years by Taylor and Maccoll in this country and by Kármán and Moore in America on the wave resistance of projectiles are encouraging signs.

Postscript

The non-specialist reader who wishes to know more of these matters may find this difficult; the writer does not know of any simple and non-technical but accurate account of high-speed flow which includes the latest advances. For the reader with a knowledge of mathematics the best general statement of the present position is undoubtedly that given by Kármán in the 10th Wright Brothers Lecture to the Institute of Aeronautical Sciences and printed in the *Journal of Aeronautical Sciences* Vol. 14, No. 7 (July 1947), but to follow this account demands a considerable knowledge of aerodynamics.

Research Report

A. W. HASLETT

Southern Stars

THE whole of stellar astronomy is based on a very limited number of possible kinds of measurement. The most obvious is measurement of position. This is the foundation of navigational astronomy, and was implicit in the invention of the calendar. The next oldest is measurement of apparent brightness. This is due to Hipparchus of Nicaea who, about 130 B.C., built an observatory at Rhodes, and made observations on about 1,000 bright stars which could be seen with the naked eye from the latitude of the Mediterranean. It is a type of knowledge which is normally taken for granted, but which enters directly into many of the more abstruse deductions which can now be made about the physical state of stars. Together with measurements or estimates of distance, it enables the absolute or true brightness of stars to be calculated, and this in turn ties in with the detailed analysis of the radiation emitted by stars, which the spectrograph makes possible. For example, the accepted classification of stars is based on a comparison of absolute brightness and spectral type. There is also a 'law', due to Sir Arthur Eddington, which enables the mass of a star to be deduced from its brightness. It follows that measurements of apparent brightness, which astronomers as well as laymen are apt to take for granted, occupy a key position in the whole structure.

Such is the background to a major and long-term undertaking on which Dr R. H. Stoy, Chief Assistant at the Royal Observatory, Cape of Good Hope, has lately reported to the Royal Astronomical Society. What is being done is nothing less than to determine the apparent magnitude or brightness of 75,000 southern hemisphere stars, and to link these through further observations at Cambridge with the standard series of stars in the neighbourhood of the North Pole to which all measurements of stellar brightness are referred. Also, because of this new and more accurate joining-up between northern and southern stars, the way will be paved for the extension of the work by other southern observatories – besides, possibly, leading to some apparently very necessary re-examination of existing northern hemisphere observations. It is quoted here as an example of a humdrum but essential type of astronomy of which little is normally heard.

The method of classification traces directly from that first introduced by Hipparchus. He began by describing the brightest stars which he knew as being of 'the first magnitude'. Stars of the next step down in brightness which he could recognise he called 'second magnitude', and so on down to the faintest which he described as 'sixth magnitude'. Rough and ready though it was, the system which he introduced has survived, with necessary modification, owing to the chance circumstance that the eye responds equally to equal proportionate increases in brightness over quite a wide range of light intensity. It was found later that his scale of magnitudes corresponded roughly to increases of 2.5 times in apparent brightness, and the modern scale is still very close to this figure. It has been so chosen that a hundredfold increase in brightness corresponds with five steps in magnitude – which gives a brightness increase for one magnitude of 2.512. But, as already indicated, the final reference is to a sequence of standard stars, near the north pole, which are internationally recognised for the purpose.

The present programme at the Cape was due in the first instance to Sir Harold Spencer Jones, now Astronomer Royal at Greenwich, but formerly H.M. Astronomer at the Cape of Good Hope. A serious start was made in 1938, and on the main work of inter-comparison 25,000 out of the original 75,000 stars have now been covered. On the other hand, various special additions to the original programme have added about another 45,000 to those on which measurements are to be made. For 'joining up', the original intention was to make use of previous brightness determinations on equatorial stars, which can be observed from both hemispheres. In practice, it has been found that no sequence of intermediate stars is available, of which the brightness is known with great enough accuracy to serve as the necessary link. The task of linking up is therefore being undertaken by Prof. R. O. Redman who, while at the Radcliffe Observatory, Pretoria, had already co-operated with the Cape Observatory in working out a series of southern standard stars which provide the immediate reference for the whole Cape observations. He has lately taken over the direction of both the university observatory and the solar physics observatory at Cambridge; and he has agreed to complete, at Cambridge, the necessary linking up with the north polar sequence of international standard stars. This will probably take about two years; but, when completed will be applicable via the Cape to all stars visible in the southern hemisphere.

(Stoy. *Monthly Notices Royal Astronomical Society*, in the press.)

X-ray Progress

Procedure for the generation of X-rays of any specified energy is to accelerate a beam of electrons to the required energy, and then stop it by allowing the electrons to hit a metal target. In *Science News V*, it was stated that the Telecommunications Research Establishment at Malvern had attained the distinction of being the first laboratory in the world to make a 'synchrotron' work – a 'synchrotron' being one possible engineering device for the acceleration of electrons – and that a larger piece of equipment capable of producing 30 million volt X-rays had been designed. Several new pieces of information can now be added. One is that two production equipments to this design are being built for the Medical Research Council. They are to be installed in Cambridge and at the Cancer Hospital, London, respectively – a disposition which will ensure that both the biological and the medical effects are adequately examined. The second is that a 'synchrotron' capable of accelerating electrons, not to 30 million volts, but to 140 million volts, is being built by the same firm for the Clarendon Laboratory, Oxford. Finally, the Telecommunications Research Establishment, which first made the 'synchrotron' work, has again demonstrated its technical competence by a similar success with a quite different type of equipment. In this, known as the linear accelerator, the electrons are accelerated by the very simple method of allowing them to travel down a metal tube in the company of centimetre radio-waves. The idea, certainly, has been common talk amongst physicists ever since the wartime development of practical and compact radio transmitters working on these very high frequencies. But, again, it is to the credit of the Malvern establishment that they should have made the idea work. It is not just a case of 'injecting' a beam of electrons into any metal tube down which radio waves happen to be travelling; but of providing precisely calculated conditions such that electrons and radio waves will travel together and in step. In the first section of the Malvern equipment to be completed, electrons have been 'injected' into such a tube at the comparatively modest energy of 45,000 volts, and have been accelerated to the equivalent of 538,000 volts. This compares with a design figure of 540,000 volts. The significance of this close agreement is that the 40-centimetres length of tube, or waveguide, which has so far been used, is only the first section of a very much longer accelerator. When complete this will be some 20 metres in length; and, with the same radio output, the electrons should be accelerated roughly in proportion. With the single section, so far tested, less than 2% of the energy of the radio transmitter was transferred to the electron beam, the remainder being wasted. With the full projected length, it is calculated that an efficiency of 80% could be secured. It is felt by physicists that some such approach offers the most economical method of attaining the highest energies, and this may also be true at the level of 30-50 million volts in which doctors are chiefly interested. But, whichever the final method, the Medical Research Council's two 'synchrotrons' will not have been wasted, since the immediate need is for experience at these greatly increased energies. For this purpose the method of production of the X-rays is immaterial, while the 'synchrotron' has the practical advantage of being relatively compact.

(Fry, R. S. Harvie, Mullet and Walkinshaw, *Nature*, 1947, 160, 351.)

History of the Earth

One more has been added to the series of shocks which physics from time to time administers to physical geology. The first was Lord Kelvin's famous calculation, based on the known facts of heat conduction and cooling by radiation, that the earth's crust would have been too hot to permit the formation of oceans at any period before about 40 million years ago. This was on the supposition – later proved false by the discovery of radio-activity – that the earth contained no source of heat within itself which could make good in part the inevitable loss of heat by radiation from the surface. The latest such shock is due to the realisation that radio-active potassium must, in the past, have made a very much bigger contribution to the earth's heat output than either uranium or thorium. It has been administered by E. Gladitsch and T. Gráf of the University of Oslo, and it affords quite a salutary demonstration of the difficulties attached to any calculation which seeks to determine conditions in the remote past from those prevailing at the present time. The change, compared with previous calculations, is due to the fact that whereas both uranium and thorium break down at a relatively slow rate, even compared with the 3,000 million years' estimated lifetime of the earth, radio-potassium breaks down considerably more quickly. The effect, working backwards in time, is naturally cumulative. If uranium and thorium had been the only significant sources of heat within the earth, the rate of release would at no time have been more than about half as great as it now is. But to account for the present surviving proportion of radio-potassium (in round figures one in every 10,000 potassium atoms) it is necessary to suppose that the initial supply must have been 1,000 times as great. This in turn leads to the conclusion that the release of heat from radio-potassium must have been 200 times greater than from uranium and thorium combined. The full implications to geology of these rather startling readjustments must take time to assess. What is more worth while to point out is that this very big increase in the estimated contribution of radio-potassium has been brought about by two comparatively small, if overdue, revisions in the numerical values obtained in some laboratory experiments in 1934. One is that the energy released in the breakdown of a single atom of radio-potassium has been increased by a factor of seven or eight. The second, and more important, is that the rate of breakdown of radio-potassium atoms has been increased by a factor of about three. Yet if these considerable, but hardly spectacular, alterations are applied cumulatively over a period of 2,400 million years – the length of time to which the calculations refer – they lead to figures of a quite different order from those previously quoted. It should perhaps be added that the various methods by which the age of the earth has been estimated are not affected by these considerations; and that, in view of their importance to geo-physics, an independent check of the present revised figures for radio-potassium is clearly desirable.

(Gladitsch and Gräf, *Physical Review*, 1947, 72, 640.)

Submarine Gravity

The use of submarines for the making of gravity surveys beneath the sea is due to Prof. Vening Meinesz of Holland, who also designed the first gravity meter sufficiently sensitive and stable to be usefully employed under such conditions. He applied the method, during a series of prolonged trips in a Dutch submarine, to measure gravity anomalies in the areas both of the East and the West Indies, and drew some conclusions about the probable growth of new mountain chains beneath the sea. Shortly before the time of Munich, the Department of Geodesy and Geophysics at Cambridge University drew up plans for a more limited investigation of conditions round the edge of the 'continental shelf' which separates Europe proper from the Atlantic. The Admiralty agreed to provide a submarine, and the expedition was planned, and even begun, in 1938. But within 36 hours of leaving port, the Munich crisis developed, and the submarine was recalled. Further plans were held up until August, 1946, when the submarine *H.M.S. Tudor* was made available for the resumed expedition, and still more lately a preliminary report has been issued.

Previous information was that, whereas sediments carried out to sea by rain and rivers had resulted in a relatively level surface to the sea bed immediately round Europe, drooping only slowly towards the edge of the 'shelf', the underlying basement rocks fell away more rapidly, so that near the edge of the 'shelf' the thickness of sediments might reach many thousands of feet. This was established by Prof. M. Ewing for the eastern seaboard of the United States, and by Dr E. C. Bullard of Cambridge for the mouth of the English Channel. The supposition, which remained unproved, was that the growing weight of sediment, driven outwards from the land by the action of the tides, had caused the basement rocks to sink more deeply into the semi-molten layer beneath, further sediment being again deposited at the lower level. The theory, in short, was that the level of the basement rocks was determined by gravitational equilibrium. The object of the *H.M.S. Tudor* expedition was to test this theory by measurements of the intensity of gravity towards the edge of the 'shelf'. Four different areas were examined, and in three of them measurements and theory were in almost perfect agreement. These were off the mouth of the English Channel, and to the west of Ireland and Scotland respectively. In each case equilibrium had been maintained; and it appeared that, without sediment, the original depth of the basement rock would have been about half as great as it now is. That, therefore, was the extent of sinking. Only the fourth area, the Bay of Biscay, was not in equilibrium. Anomalies here were attributed to horizontal pressure connected with the coastal ranges.

(Browne, *Observatory*, 1947, 67, 173.)

The Heart in Starvation

It is no secret that the experience of doctors and research teams, both in occupied Europe and in the rehabilitation of those who had been in Japanese prisoner-of-war camps, resulted in a good deal of new information about the be- haviour of the body under near-starvation conditions, and also during rehabilitation. In addition, many of the results are now available of an experiment which was carried out in the Laboratory of Physiological Hygiene of the University of Minnesota, with fit young Americans as volunteer subjects.

The most general point which has emerged is that the body can balance food intake and energy consumption at a considerably lower level than had before been realised, and when this position has been reached no further loss of weight takes place. Loss of weight in itself reduces the amount of fuel – from food or fat reserves – which must be 'burnt' to maintain normal bodily processes. In addition, the individ- ual learns to keep his avoidable output of muscular energy to the lowest level possible. Both factors help towards the attainment of a new balance, and both in the Minnesota experiment and in the Hong Kong civilian internment camp this was reached when weight had fallen by one quarter from its original level. Equally, it was found during rehab- ilitation that time was needed for a normal balance of chemical activity to be re-established. Professor Beattie, for example, of the Royal College of Surgeons, has pointed out that during the first stages of rehabilitation, practically the whole of the protein eaten as food, which one would normally expect to be largely utilised in tissue replacement and 'building up', was in fact burnt as 'fuel' – even although enough Calories to meet energy requirements were being otherwise supplied.

The most detailed and interesting findings are, however, those at Minnesota on the response of the heart. The traditional assumption in the past has been that, during starvation or near-starvation, the heart and other vital organs were 'protected' from damage for as long as a necessary minimum of nourishment was available. The experience of the 32 fit young men who went through the Minnesota experiment shows clearly that this is not the case. The outline of the test was that they were observed first through three months of normal diet, during which period they required on the average 3,200 Calories for energy balance; then for six months with a food intake of 1,700 Calories, by which time they had lost 24% of their original weight; and finally, during rehabilitation, for three months of controlled diet, and a further five during which they could eat what they liked. X-ray photographs, taken from different angles, were used to record the physical volume of the heart at all stages, and other measurements enabled the output of work by the heart to be calculated. It was found that, when adjustment to semi-starvation had been completed, the volume of the heart had been reduced by 16%, the number of strokes per minute by 32%, and the heart's output of physical work by as much as 49%. Also, the margin of safety represented by unused oxygen, still left in the blood after circulation, had been brought down by one half. With such drastic changes, a quick return to normal would scarcely be expected. In practice three months of controlled feeding sufficed only to get the heart nearly, but not quite back to normal in size, with practically no improvement in its capacity for work. Nor did the inclusion of extra vitamins and protein in the diet make any noticeable difference. By the end of five months, of which the last two had been on unlimited diet, the heart size was slightly greater than it had been originally, but capacity for work was still 10% below normal and only half of the lost margin of oxygen safety had been made good. Finally, at the end of 32 weeks, only very slight signs of abnormality could be detected.

Climate and Food

Evidence suggesting that dietary preferences are automatically adjusted to suit climatic conditions has been obtained at the Medical Clinic of the University of Pecs, Hungary. The basis of the experiment was to offer different groups of mice the choice of three different food mixtures at three different temperatures. Each food mixture was composed as to one-third of a standard mixture, which provided in itself the whole of the accessory factors needed for health, while the remaining two-thirds was either starch, milk protein (casein) or fat. The mice were free to eat as they chose, and at normal room temperature took roughly two-thirds of their total calories from the fatty food mixture. The main comparison was, however, between their feeding habits at moderately low temperatures (50-52 degrees F.) and approximately tropical conditions (84-91 degrees F.). The interest of the experiment was that, although differences in total consumption ranged from about 20 to about 40%, in all cases practically the whole difference was due to an increase or decrease in consumption of starch, the amount of protein and fat eaten remaining approximately constant under all conditions. The mice, in other words, did precisely as any dietetic expert would have advised – taking as much protein and fat as they needed, and then using starch as a 'buffer' to make up the balance of their calorie requirements. A generation ago, 'instinct' would no doubt have been put forward as the explanation. Today, some form of chemical control appears more plausible. And since the activity of the thyroid gland may increase as much as three-fold at low temperatures, it is suggested that it is through the thyroid gland that food tastes are thus regulated. But, although the experimental facts appear clear enough, it should be pointed out that the suggested explanation is no more than a speculation.

(Donhoffer and Vonotzky, *American Journal of Physiology*, 1947, 150, 329.)

Control of the Tsetse Fly

Control of the mosquito and the locust having been proved practicable, hopes have naturally been aroused that the even more difficult and equally important problem of the tsetse fly would also be solved. As the carrier of nagana disease of cattle, this is generally regarded as the most serious remaining brake on the future progress and development of tropical Africa. Exceptional interest was therefore taken in a recent film demonstration by Dr P. J. du Toit, Director of the Union of South Africa Veterinary Service, of the use of D.D.T. from the air against the tsetse fly.

D.D.T. was first tried in the form of a liquid emulsion, sprayed from the air. Thus used, it was shown by fly-trap counts to reduce the tsetse fly population in the proportion of 9,000 to 600 three months after treatment. This was a big improvement, but not enough to achieve the intended purpose of local eradication. To get better results, it was realised, it would be necessary to get the D.D.T. to the underside of the foliage, where the fly chiefly sheltered. Further experiments were therefore carried out in which the heat of the engine was used to vaporise the D.D.T., and the insecticide ejected from the aircraft as a fine smoke. With this treatment the fly population in the same area was further reduced in the proportion of 600 to 3 – so that the overall reduction was now about 3,000 to one.

Procedure is for aircraft to fly at a height of between 50 and 75 feet – little more than tree-top height – and in arrow-head formation. Each aircraft can cover a strip of 70 yards in width, and a flight of six aircraft has been used. It has been found that the slight breeze of early morning helps to

carry the resulting smoke blanket in under the trees. But by
ordinary standards conditions must be calm. Practice so far
has been to make six successive flights at fortnightly intervals, and to treat residual fly patches with smoke generators
carried by hand through the bush and operated from the
ground. Cost is estimated at 18s. per acre – small enough,
certainly, in relation to farming output, but large when
multiplied by the total acreage of tropical Africa.

Fortunately for Dr du Toit, the Union problem with
which he is immediately concerned can be treated in isolation
from the wider one of tropical Africa. In place of almost
unlimited areas, he has to deal with about 1,000 square
miles of active infestation, split up into some three different
areas, all in Zululand, and a further perhaps 4,000 square
miles of potential infestation. Also, between the most
northerly of these Zululand areas and the main belt stretch-
ing from east to west across the whole breadth of Africa,
there is a gap of about 200 miles in which no tsetse have
been found in recent years. The aim, therefore, is complete
eradication within these comparatively limited areas, and
for this purpose the cost of the air treatment which has been
tried would not be unreasonable. For the moment, treated
areas are being 'sealed' by the total removal of all bush
within a two-miles belt, and a watch is being kept to see
what happens to the small remaining fly population. It was
possible, Dr du Toit thought, that natural enemies would
do the rest – but not all his audience felt the same optimism.

Of the other possible methods of control which have been
attempted, game extermination has aroused the greatest
controversy. The basis for it is the supposition that tsetse
fly (of which, incidentally, there are twenty different species)
can obtain nourishment from wild game as well as from
cattle. It is commonly believed, therefore – and with some
reason – that wild game act as a reservoir both of the fly
and of the nagana disease which the fly carries. It has been
pointed out, however, that further research is needed to
establish the contribution made by different game species,

and that there is no case on scientific grounds for the indiscriminate slaughter of all alike.

Prof. P. A. Buxton of the London School of Hygiene and Tropical Medicine, who presided at Dr du Toit's film demonstration, drew attention also to the fact that in East Africa selective clearing of as little as five per cent of the bush had been enough to bring about complete local elimination of the fly. The difficulty is that since local conditions naturally vary, and that over quite small areas, a series of detailed studies by 'fly-minded' investigators would be necessary. Similarly, under the savannah conditions of Northern Nigeria, where during the hot season the tsetse fly barely survives, a relatively small amount of clearance can produce big results. The feeling of the meeting was that, although no single method is likely to solve the whole problem, Dr du Toit's smoke-spray attack is 'well worth trying under as many conditions as possible'.

Midge Investigation

Nearer home, the Universities of Glasgow and St Andrews have lately combined to begin a seven-years' investigation of the midge, the activities of which have been more taken for granted than studied. The fact, however, is that midge infestation could be a serious handicap to the development of much of the western Highlands, and that comparatively little is known about its biology. This applies both to the distribution of species, of which some thirty are recognised, although most of the human biting is attributed to one, and to the life-cycle and habits of the insects. For example, although the adult insect can be kept alive for up to two months in the laboratory with access to carbohydrate food, it is not known whether under natural conditions the developed insect takes any further food than the blood meal needed by the female for the development of her eggs. Little is known either about the conditions under which eggs are laid, although damp soil is thought to be 'probable'. A hutted laboratory has been established, as a centre for field studies, at Rossdhu, Loch Lomond, and various laboratory investigations are being carried out in the University of St Andrews.

Embryo Nutrition

Increased use is being made of the radio-active tracer method of studying the developing embryo. It is particularly well suited to this purpose since the capacity to 'label' atoms of particular chemical elements in the mother is precisely what is needed for the investigation of the transfer of those same elements to the embryo. Earlier work in the United States, mainly between 1941 and 1942, did little more than illustrate the scope of the method and was interrupted by Pearl Harbour when the most interesting stage appeared likely to be reached. One such test, with radio-calcium in mice, confirmed that there was a transfer to the foetus of calcium which had previously been 'fixed' in the bones of the mother, and showed that the last calcium to be absorbed was also the first to be released for transfer. This was in the Crocker Radiation Laboratory at Berkeley, California, which later took a leading part in investigating the absorption of plutonium and fission products formed in the uranium pile in relation to safety precautions for atomic energy workers. Another such experiment, carried out at Rochester University, showed that the time interval between the feeding of iron to the mother and the appearance of radio-activity in the blood of the embryo was only forty minutes. The text-book description of the formation of blood cells in the embryo was that the red cells of the mother travelled as such through the umbilical cord to the embryo, and were there broken down, and the iron which they contained re-used in the formation of the embryo's own red cells. But the shortness of the observed interval made it unlikely to the point of impossibility that this explanation could be correct. Finally, Dr P. E. Nielson of the University of Wisconsin carried out a similar and preliminary study of the transfer of phosphorus.

Greater availability of radio-active supplies is now leading to an increased interest in the method, for this as for other research purposes, and at a recent meeting of the Biochemical Society, Dr G. Popják of the National Institute for Medical Research described the results of a more detailed investigation in the case of phosphorus. The problem is similar to that raised, and already partly answered, in the case of iron. Can the embryo make use of simple inorganic materials, and if so how are they converted into organic form? In particular, what is the origin of the complex phospholipids – fat-like substances – needed by every cell? Dr Nielson's work had already suggested that inorganic phosphorus could be used. Dr Popják has now shown further that both from the liver and the placenta of the embryo it is possible to extract phospholipids which, weight for weight, are more highly radio-active than the blood plasma of the mother, into which the test injection had been made. This could scarcely happen unless in these organs, at least, the embryo was doing its own building up. Similar experiments have been carried out on rats, guinea pigs, and rabbits, and they all support the same conclusion. There is also more limited evidence suggesting that all the organs of the embryo, and not only the liver and placenta, are capable of the same building up process. This was obtained by direct injection of the embryo with radio-active phosphate.

(Popják, *Biochemical Journal*, in the press.)

Ultrasonics

DR GABRIELE RABEL

THE terms 'Ultrasonics' and 'Supersonics' have been buzzing about recently in the news, and especially the 'Bat Case' has aroused considerable interest. The subject of this article is to give a brief account of what ultrasonic waves (USW) can do, but as I have noticed here and there some confusion attached to the terms ultra- and supersonic, it seems desirable to begin by clearing the terminological ground.

Ultrasonic vibrations are of the same type as sound vibrations, but have a frequency too high to be sensed as sound by the human ear.

The threshold of audible sound is 30 vibrations per second. Its upper limit is said to be 20,000, but for old people it is considerably lower. What is above 20,000 is not audible to the human ear, but is ultrasonic.

In papers written in English these high frequencies are often described as 'supersonic', but 'ultrasonic' is preferable for three reasons: this word has chronological priority, it matches the German 'Ultraschall' and the French 'ondes ultra-sonores' and airminded people use the term 'supersonic' for a velocity not for a frequency. What do they mean by a 'supersonic velocity'? They tell us, it makes a difference whether a jet of gas or a bullet or aircraft moves through air 'faster than sound' or slower. They do not mean that it may be important to hear an aircraft before it arrives, but that the aircraft (or air-jet) itself is decisively influenced by its own 'supersonic' velocity. How on earth does sound come into the problem? The answer is: not at all.

Every pressure change, every disturbance, periodic or non-periodic, spreads in air with the same velocity. Sound is a pressure change. Therefore sound, too, spreads with the same velocity. But as this latter fact is irrelevant, the term 'supersonic velocity' is misleading, and I propose to use the non-committal terms 'Supervelocity' and 'Subvelocity' for speeds above and below the general 'Disturbance Velocity'.

If an aircraft moves with subvelocity through air, the disturbance created by it runs ahead and prepares the way for the coming traveller. If, however, the aircraft travels faster than the disturbance it has created, the result is that a cone of highly-compressed air (called a shockwave though it is not really a wave) envelops the bow of the craft and acts as a resistance.

Similarly if an air-jet moves with supervelocity, entirely novel conditions arise. The jet breaks into segments, and if a tiny cavity, say a tube of 1 mm. diameter and the same length, closed on one end, is introduced into certain parts of these segments, the cavity hurls the air back periodically and the periods are of ultrasonic frequency.

This is one way of producing USW. One further gets them from a Galton whistle, or jingling keys, or from Magnetostrictive or Piezoelectric Oscillators.

Magnetostriction is the periodic contraction of a nickel rod in an alternating magnetic field. The end of the rod emits high frequency waves.

Piezoelectricity is an electric charge developed on the surface of certain crystals, including quartz, under pressure. If, conversely, an alternating voltage is applied to a plate cut out of such a crystal, the plate contracts and expands periodically, causing compressions and rarefactions in the surrounding medium.

Every body has a 'natural frequency' (*Eigenschwingung*). If the rhythm of the externally imposed alternating voltage coincides with the very high natural frequency of the quartz plate, the maximum effect, Resonance, is obtained, and the vibrations thus produced have enormous and astounding effects.

The energy of sound waves is proportional to the square of the frequency; that is why vibrations up to a million cycles per second or more are so powerful. E. Meyer has computed that if an orator talked without interruption for 150 years, the sound energy expended would be just enough to boil water for a cup of tea. But water traversed by USW boils an egg in a jiffy. R. Wood tells us that the acceleration at the surface of a vibrating crystal, though the amplitude be only 0.008 mm., can amount to 40,000 kilometres per second per second.*

Wood and Loomis reported, among other spectacular results, that in a dish of oil with a piezoquartz at the bottom, the oil drops surged up to 40 cm. height as from a miniature volcano. They worked with 2 kilowatt power at 50,000 volts. Later Grützmacher constructed piezocrystals in the form of spherical mirrors and at the focus of such a quartz mirror a power of only $\frac{1}{2}$-kilowatt at 2,400 volts makes the oil jump even higher.

A recent development is the construction of ultrasonic lenses.

Up to World War I, piezoelectricity was a laboratory curiosity. In 1917, Langevin constructed a device which made it possible to send out a narrow beam of USW under water for signalling and for determining the position of submarines by the echo method. USW are well suited for the purpose because they are very little absorbed in water – much less than in air.

The echo principle is also used for measuring the depth of the sea. Utilising multiple echoes it is possible, not only to get a profile of the sea bottom, but even to decide whether it consists of sand, mud or clay.

George Godwin in his book *Marconi* describes an interesting Admiralty order received in 1942 for a Submarine Buoy radiating ultrasonic signals with changing pulse rates to prevent identification, sufficient for bearings to be taken

* If n body moved out into space with such an acceleration, it would acquire a velocity of 40,000 km. p.s. in 10 seconds and would by this time be 2 million km. away.

on, but not to be picked up by the enemy, blowing itself up if fished up, transmitting every one or two hours day and night but only for 14 days in the 28, with the task of acting as Radio Underwater Lighthouses. In Sicily and at Anzio these buoys guided radio-equipped landing craft to their appointed positions on the beaches. In the English Channel and in the North Sea they marked sunken wrecks. Before D-Day these ultrasonic buoys were laid off the French shore to guide the ships through the enemy minefields without arousing the suspicion of a highly-nervous enemy.

The principle of sending out USW pulses and measuring the reflection time is used in industry for finding flaws in metal blocks or the level of a liquid in a metal tank.

A liquid or solid traversed by an ultrasonic wave system acts on light like a diffraction grating, the lines of compression being lines of greater density. If USW are thus applied to anisotropic crystals, they give rise to interference images which reveal at one glance the elastic symmetries of the crystal. Bergmann who shows some beautiful pictures of this type in his book on *Ultrasonics* emphasizes that one and the same sample yields at once a complete system of all the constants in a way not obtainable with any previous method.

The diffraction spectra produced by USW are also used in England by the Scophony system of television.

The extreme shortness of the ultrasonic waves down to the order of 0.00055 mm., that of visible light, makes them handy as a measuring device, while the long, audible sound waves are unfit for laboratory purposes. Instruments applying USW can be used as saccharimeters. They are also used to determine the velocity of sound in different substances; which in its turn reveals many physico-chemical characteristics of the medium, such as compressibility, chemical structure, concentration, specific heat. In soil analysis, frequent shaking and centrifuging is required to disperse the colloids from the soil grains. But treatment with USW disperses them in a few minutes.

Immiscible liquids such as oil/water or mercury/water are

transformed by USW into very stable emulsions. Colloidal systems with any desired size of particles can be obtained by USW radiation, especially in combination with electrolysis. Nitrogen can be dispersed in steel for hardening purposes, nickel molecules are loosened up, facilitating magnetic reversal – but to what extent such methods are applied in industry it is difficult to ascertain. The photographic industry, it seems, makes extensive use of this property of USW to produce fine and homogeneous emulsions.

While USW energetically disperse solids and liquids in water, they have the contrary effect on systems called aerosols, such as fog, mist, dust, smoke – solids or liquids finely dispersed in air. Such substances when irradiated by USW are instantaneously clotted together and sink down leaving the air immaculately clean. Why this opposite effect? The answer is that a startlingly revolutionary process called *Cavitation* occurs in water but cannot occur in a gas. Cavitation so disrupts a liquid that even if it was formerly gas-free, it is then interspersed with gas bubbles. When a cavity collapses, pressures of thousands of atmospheres may be developed, and high kinetic energies concentrated at very small spots create devastating mechanical effects. Cavitation is produced by high speed propellers and causes heavy erosions in armour plates, a headache for naval engineers.

But cavitation is also produced by USW during the expansion phase. It is not the formation of a cavity, but its vehement collapse which causes such turbulent processes as emulsification. It also brings oxygen into a reactive state and various chemical reactions, e.g. the formation of hydrogen peroxide, may thus be indirectly stimulated by USW. Liquids often emit visible light during cavitation. Obviously some kind of exciting or electrifying action must go on in those cavities. If cavitation is prevented, which can be done either by working in a vacuum or under high external pressure, USW neither liquefy gels nor emulsify oils, but in the emulsification of water and mercury, cavitation has no part.

Liquids with a low boiling point can be made to distil at room temperature when radiated with USW *in vacuo:* as the liquid boils in the cavities, the gas bubbles quickly combine to larger bubbles and climb up.

If small living organisms are exposed to USW, they are mostly torn to pieces or burnt or otherwise destroyed. But what really happens is not yet quite clear. In some cases, cavitation has been observed in the medium, in others it has not. Living beings exposed at the same time to violent compressions and rarefactions of the medium, cannot endure the enormous tension. But if they are small enough to be collected in the nodes of standing wave patterns, they may rest there happily and unharmed – as long as no cavitation occurs.

If a liquid which swarms with bacteria is exposed to sound waves, the cells explode quickly and the antigens, otherwise difficult to extract, are liberated.

In Japan, a verminous parasite used to ruin billions of silkworm cocoons annually. If the affected cocoons are immersed in water and bombarded with USW for 3 minutes, the parasites withdraw into the body of the worm and quickly die there from suffocation.

USW are further reported to deprive yeast cells of their power of multiplication, luminous bacteria of their luminosity, pathogenic bacteria of their virulence, to sterilize milk and to give milk a 'soft curd character'.

Everybody would expect that powerful rays which can be focussed would be valuable medical assistants, and indeed the literature abounds with pious hopes in this direction. But the only paper I have discovered that tells of real cures is one by Pohlman, Richter and Parow (*Medizinische Wochenschrift*, 1939) who successfully treated cases of Sciatica and Plexus Neuralgia.*

While the production and exploitation of USW is a new adventure for us human beings, animals have used them since

* More clinical experiments will be needed to know if this treatment has real value. *Ed.*

time immemorial. The hearing apparatus of many animals is obviously sensitive to these vibrations. When Galton blew his high frequency whistle, spectators who heard nothing, but saw his dog obey the call, suspected occult doings. Ultrasonic utterances have been studied in grasshoppers, but the best examined case so far is that of the bats. When they fly through dark woods or long tortuous caves, they do just what Langevin did first in 1917, namely send out pulses of USW and then decide from the time and direction of the echo where there is an object lurking in the dark.

The Americans Pierce, Griffin and Galambos made bats fly through barriers of parallel wires in complete darkness and recorded the hits or misses. When only the mouth was covered, the bats were as unaware of the wire as with plugged ears. When only one ear was covered, they lost their pluck. They need both ears for localisation, just as we do.

Bats emit three distinctly different types of sound: (1) a shrill audible cry (7,000 cycles per second, lasting $\frac{1}{4}$-second or less) not contributing to obstacle avoidance; (2) an ultrasonic cry (ranging from 30-70 kilocycles, lasting 0.15 seconds, unfailingly accompanied by (3) a feeble click which, when the bat is in flight, is repeated so quickly as to be noticed as a buzz.

Remarkable is the way bats vary their ultrasonic utterances according to where they are and what they are doing. They utter less than 10 ultrasonic cries per second, when sitting on the wall and preparing for the flight; 20-30 when flying through unobstructed space; 50-60 when approaching the obstacle; then there is a sudden drop to 30, and when this drop happens, you know they have got through unscathed. If it does not happen, this is a bad sign.

The audible and the inaudible cries can be emitted at once, but as the audible is never heard during flight, the inaudible obviously is no overtone. Each bat has a 'personal' voice of its own, an individual combination of frequencies and relative intensities. This 'significant cry' comes from bats preparing to fly or to alight, from caged bats seeking escape and cave bats awakened from sleep.

How do the bats produce all these sounds? They are certain to come out of the mouth, and they are probably produced in the larynx. No explanation was found for the independence of the audible and ultrasonic tones or for the extraordinarily high rate of emission of the latter.

Anti-Vitamins

PROFESSOR JOHN YUDKIN

MANY substances are now known which antagonise the action of certain of the vitamins. Such substances may, in an animal, produce the signs of vitamin deficiency, even though the diet contains what is normally an adequate amount of the vitamin. In so far, therefore, as these 'anti-vitamins' may occur in natural foodstuffs, they are clearly of importance in the field of practical dietetics. But a closer study of them, and of the history of their discovery, shows that they have a far wider theoretical and practical interest. An understanding of them is, for example, necessary for those who are concerned in the present intensive search for new drugs for the treatment of human disease.

Most of the anti-vitamins belong to the group of 'metabolic analogues' or competitive inhibitors. To understand how this type of substance functions we shall have to go back a long way through quite unexpected paths. We might begin with Ehrlich, who, nearly 50 years ago, developed his 'side-chain' theory to account for the phenomenon of specific immunity.

When a person develops an immunity to a bacterial infection like typhoid fever, his blood becomes capable of re-acting with the typhoid bacteria, and making them 'agglutinate', or clump together. What has happened is that, during the infection, the typhoid bacteria (the antigen) made the infected patient produce in his own blood a specific antibody so that whenever the blood again comes into contact with typhoid bacteria, the antibody reacts with the bacteria, which then agglutinate and so are rendered harmless.

According to Ehrlich's theory, the reaction between the antibody developed in the blood and the antigen of the

bacteria occurs by a union between the two; the fact that
antigens for different bacteria combine with different and
very specific antibodies in the host is supposed to be due
to the two substances being of such a structure that the one
just fits into the other (Fig. 3). No other antibody will combine with this antigen because no other will have a structure
which fits the appropriate group or 'side-chain' of the antigen.

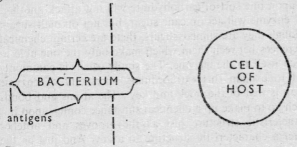

Figure 3a—Bacteria entering body of host.

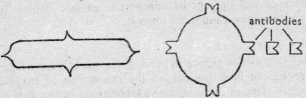

Figure 3b—Bacterial antigens stimulate cells of host to produce
antibodies, which circulate in the bloodstream.

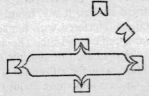

Figure 3c—Further bacterial invasion leads to combination of host
antibodies with bacterial antigens,
and bacteria are agglutinated.

Specificity of Enzymes

A similar idea was developed by biochemists to explain how it is that enzymes, like antibodies, are very 'fussy' about the exact constitution of the substance (substrate) with which they react. For example, the pancreas makes several enzymes, which digest proteins, carbohydrates and fats. But the enzyme which digests proteins will not digest fats or carbohydrates. More than this, an enzyme which will act upon one sort of carbohydrate will not attack another. One enzyme will act on cane sugar, but not on malt sugar; although they are similar sugars, there are certain chemical differences between them which make only the one able to attach itself to the enzyme. The simile which is commonly used to explain this extraordinary specificity of enzyme action is that of the 'lock and key'. The atoms and bonds which go to make up a chemical substance confer upon it a characteristic structure just as the grooves and notches confer a characteristic structure to a key. And just as the key will only fit a lock for which it is made, so a chemical substance will only fit its appropriate enzyme. Unless it fits, the enzyme cannot act upon it.

Enzyme Inhibition

With this sort of picture in mind, many workers have been carrying out investigations on the mechanism of enzyme reaction. One of the most active laboratories in this field is at Cambridge, where Dr Stephenson and her colleagues have been studying the enzymes of bacteria for more than 20 years. In one of these studies, it was found by Dr Quastel that certain substances interfered with the action of an enzyme upon its own specific substrate. The action which he was studying was the oxidation of succinic acid by the enzyme succinic oxidase, and the substance which interfered was malonic acid. One curious thing about the interference was that the degree of interference did not depend so much on the absolute amount of malonic acid that was present, as on the relative amount of malonic to succinic acid. When malonic acid was added to the active enzyme, the rate of oxidation of succinic acid was reduced, but it was considerably restored if more succinic acid was added and again inhibited if more malonic acid was added.

$$CH_2\ COOH$$
$$|$$
$$CH_2 \cdot COOH$$
Succinic acid

$$CH_2\ COOH$$
$$|$$
$$COOH$$
Malonic acid

Figure 4

It seemed as if there was a competition between these two substances. Because of their similar structure, either could apparently combine with the enzyme, although only the succinic acid could be acted upon (Fig. 4). Since there was only a limited amount of enzyme, the combination of malonic acid with the enzyme meant that there was less of the enzyme available to combine with the succinic acid. One can picture the molecules jostling each other for places on the enzyme. And one can see how it is that the amount of oxidation which occurs depends on the relative amounts of the two competing types of molecules.

Sulpha Drugs

A similar explanation was advanced by Dr Woods, who had also been a pupil of Dr Stephenson, to account for the action of the sulphonamide type of drug on bacteria. Bacteria may, like animals, require particular nutrients – vitamins – for their growth, and one of these, required by several species of bacteria, is a substance called para-aminobenzoic acid. Dr Woods was struck by the chemical resemblance of several of the sulpha drugs to this substance, and suggested that these drugs act by competitive inhibition (Fig. 5). That is, they get in the way of the vitamin wherever it is in the bacteria that it carries out its function. This theory, that the sulpha drugs act as anti-vitamins for certain species of bacteria, is supported by the fact that bacteria prevented from growing by the addition to their culture medium of

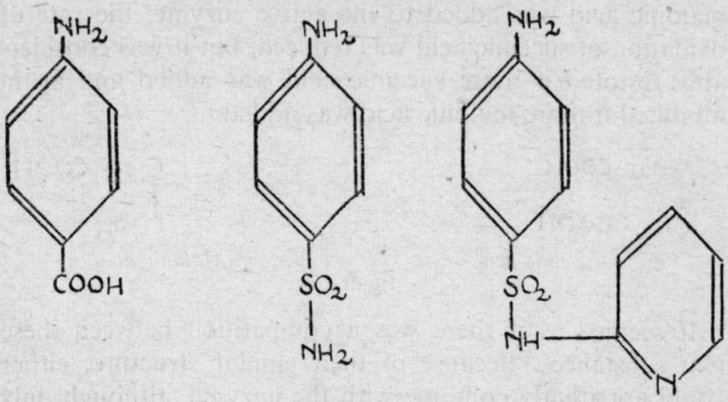

A.   B.   C.

A *para-aminobenzoic acid*.   B *sulphanilamide*.   C *sulphapyridine*.

Figure 5

one of the sulpha drugs, are able to grow again if para-aminobenzoic acid is added.

Vitamins and their Competitors

Since that time, a number of substances have been found which act as anti-vitamins in animals. Many of them are substances which have been specially synthesised so as to be chemically similar to vitamins; others have been found to occur in nature. An interesting feature of the synthetic substances is that, until they are tested, one does not know whether they act as vitamins or as anti-vitamins. A substance acts as a vitamin if its structure is sufficiently similar for it to take part in all the essential functions of the cell in which the original vitamin is involved. On the other hand, it acts as an anti-vitamin if its structure is sufficiently similar for it to attach itself to the appropriate points of action of the vitamin, but not enough for it to fulfil its functions: in this way it simply displaces the vitamin and may produce deficiency disease in the animal.

One of the first examples of this which was discovered, is a substance – pyrithiamine – which acts antagonistically to vitamin-B_1 (thiamine). A glance at the formulae shows

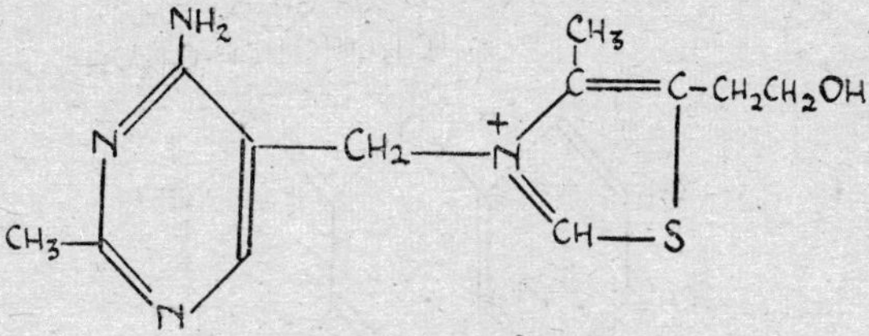

Vitamin B₁ (thiamine).

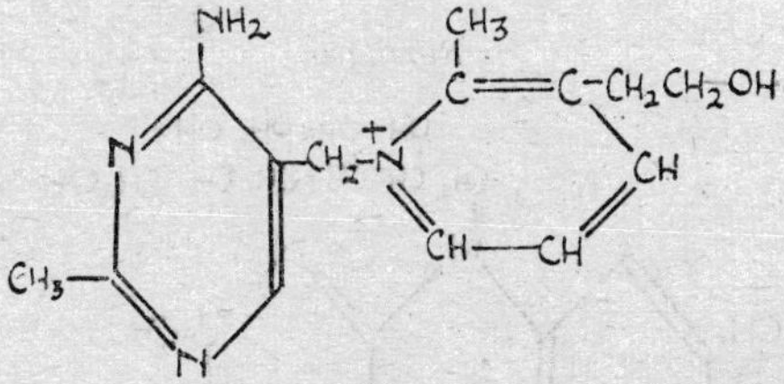

Pyrithiamine.
Figure 6

how closely similar are the chemical structures of these two substances (Fig. 6). Pyrithiamine fed to mice rapidly produces deficiency of vitamin-B₁ – produces it, in fact, more quickly and more severely than does feeding the mice on a diet deficient in the vitamin. If the amount of vitamin-B₁ in the diet is increased, no deficiency is produced; if more pyrithiamine is added, deficiency again occurs and again may be avoided by increasing the dietary supply of the vitamin still further. In other words, this anti-vitamin acts as a competitive inhibitor just like the sulpha drugs in bacteria.

Many similar substances have been discovered or prepared and we now have anti-vitamins for a great many of the vitamins. Many of them are known to act only on bacteria but quite a number can be shown to produce their effect in animals (e.g. Fig. 7). It would be a formidable task to enumerate all of these, so we must be content with choosing some of the more interesting examples.

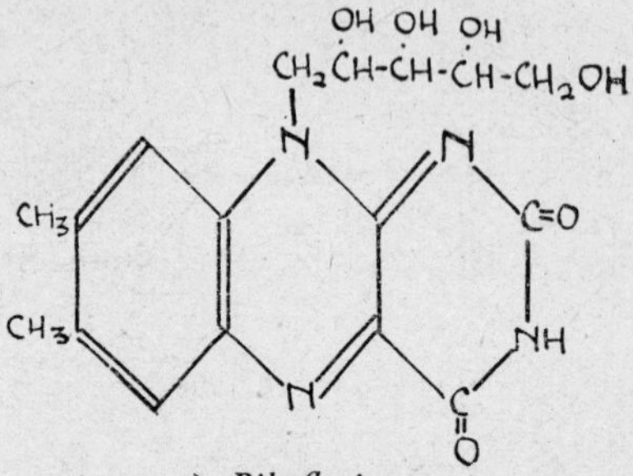

Riboflavin.

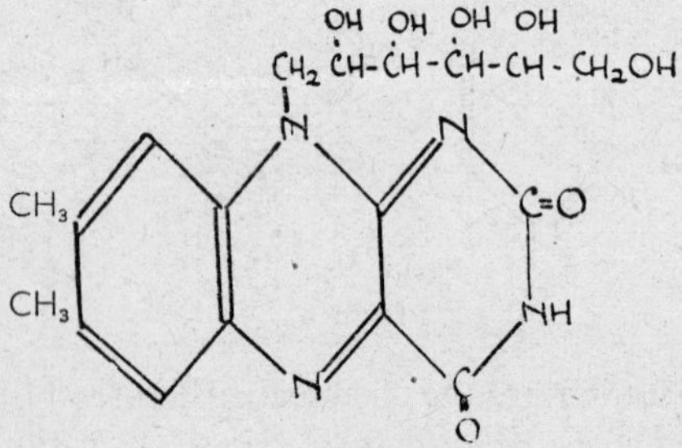

Galactoflavin.
Figure 7

The Sweet-Clover Disease

One such example concerns a naturally occurring anti-vitamin which has considerable practical importance. Some 20 years ago a disease was observed in the prairies of Canada and the Western States of America in which the cattle suffered from hæmorrhages severe enough to cause many deaths. A relatively small operation such as castration, or even a scratch from a fence, often led to bleeding which sometimes could not be stopped. At first, this disease was thought to be due to some sort of infection, but intensive search failed to reveal any possible disease-producing organism. After a time it was noticed that the disease seemed to be associated with the consumption by the cattle of spoiled sweet clover, and animals could often be cured if this food was removed from their diet. Attempts were then made to extract what was apparently a toxic material from the spoiled clover, and after a great deal of difficult chemical work, a substance was isolated which seemed to be the cause of the disease. This substance, dicoumarol, was found to cause bleeding in experimental animals because of an interference with the clotting power of the blood. The effects produced by feeding dicoumarol were exactly similar to those produced by a deficiency of vitamin-K, and administration of vitamin-K overcame the toxic effects of dicoumarol (Fig. 8). The spoiled sweet clover, then, produces its

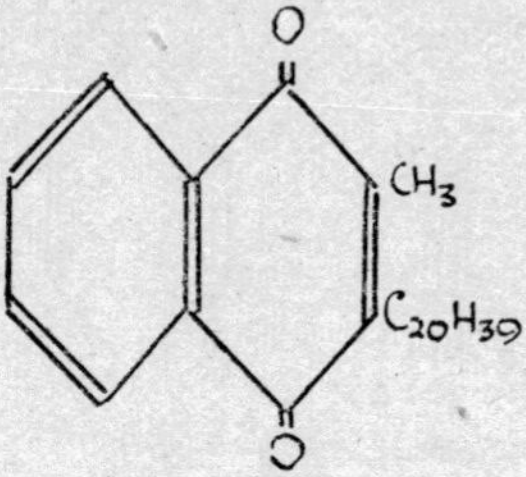

Vitamin K.

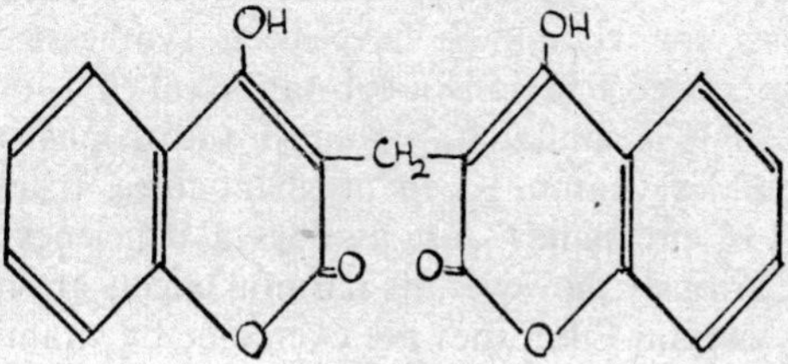

Dicoumarol.
Figure 8

effect because it contains dicoumarol, which leads to a deficiency of vitamin-K in the cattle owing to its action as a competitive inhibitor of the vitamin.

There are two further points of interest in connection with this. One is that dicoumarol is now being used in medicine in conditions where it is desirable deliberately to decrease the clotting power of the blood; amongst such conditions are coronary thrombosis and thrombophlebitis. The second interesting point is the possible anti-vitamin-K activity of salicylates or aspirin. Very large doses of these drugs are given in some conditions, notably rheumatic fever, and it has occasionally been noticed that this is followed by a tendency for bleeding from the alimentary canal. If such effects occur nowadays, they are treated with vitamin K. The chemical structure of salicylates and aspirin shows that they might well be expected to act antagonistically to vitamin-K (Fig. 9).

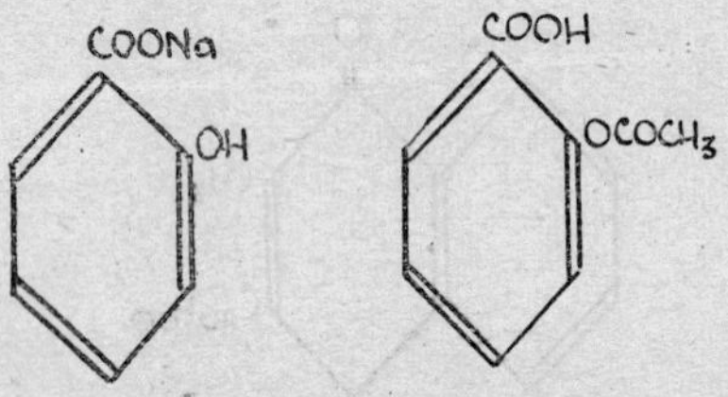

Sodium salicylate.　　　　*Aspirin.*

Figure 9

Apart from the naturally occurring dicoumarol, other antagonists for vitamin-K have been synthesised in the laboratory: one of these is a substance called α-tocopherol quinone. This is similar to vitamin-E (α-tocopherol) but it also resembles vitamin-K. In pregnant mice, it leads to a cessation of pregnancy, just as does a deficiency of vitamin-E. Curiously, however, its harmful effects are not overcome by vitamin-E but they are overcome by vitamin-K. So here we have a substance chemically similar to two vitamins, which causes a deficiency of one vitamin, but whose effects are only counteracted by the other.

Vitamin or Anti-Vitamin?

It was mentioned earlier that a substance made so as to resemble the chemical structure of a vitamin might not necessarily act as an anti-vitamin, but might actually be

Plate 1. Recording methods of cultivation, land usage, and boundaries. Note the ploughing marks, footpaths, and cultivated strips in these fields ; and the farm buildings left-centre.   *R.C.A.F. photograph.*

Plates 2 and 3. Caen, Normandy. The typical Air Photograph is a mosaic collection of details which are only properly appreciated when viewed under high magnification and stereoscopically. This photograph of Caen – taken during the battle of Normandy – was of tactical value in that it revealed the usable roads, etc., in the town. Photographs of this type reproduced in the Press were normally made from copy negatives and reproduced on too small a scale to reveal the wealth of detail recorded. The rectangular area outlined in white is reproduced in greater detail opposite to show the damage to the bridge. *Crown Copyright*.

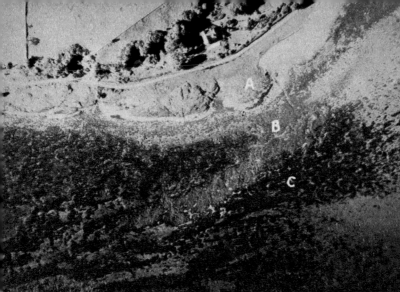

Plates 4 and 5. Detection of commercially valuable seaweed by making comparison photos by green light (see above) and infra-red radiation (below). The green filter photograph shows a belt of probable rock weed B, and a belt of bottom weed C. That belt B is weed and not dark-toned or wet bare rock is clear from the infra-red print, on which the weed appears very bright owing to its high reflectivity in deep red light. Bare rock (A), or sand and shingle appear dark on the infra-red print in contrast to the weed. Underwater weed (C) is invisible on the infra-red print except for isolated plants covered by a few inches of water; stereoscopic examination of green prints, however, confirms bottom weed at (C). *Courtesy of Majors P. K. Wiggs, P. E. Conant and the Army Photographic Research Unit.*

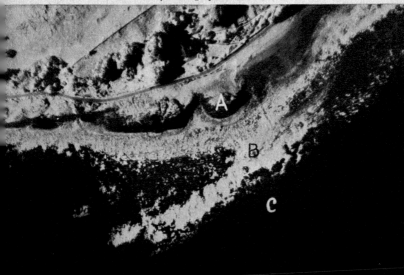

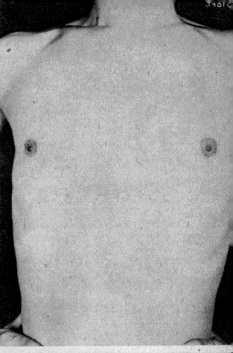

Plates 6 and 7. The Human Chest, above as seen by the eye, below as recorded by infra-red photography. The surface layers of the skin, like the haze which obscures the detail of a distant landscape, the surface layers of oil paintings, and a large variety of dark pigments, all transmit infra-red rays and so permit the photographer to record detail invisible to the eye and the normal photographic emulsion. Here the method has a medical application – the recording of the superficial veins running hidden beneath the skin. It is of value in the study of varicose veins, the dilatation of veins of the breast in some heart diseases, certain skin diseases (e.g. eczema and lupus); and for recording the condition of the iris of the eye through an opaque cornea. There is a common misconception that infra-red photography will penetrate clouds and fogs. In fact, as a comparison of Plates 4 and 5 demonstrates, photographable infra-red radiation is absorbed by water and the infra-red camera is nearly as helpless as the human eye in fogs. Infra-red does, however, penetrate heat haze and when long-distance infra-red photographs are made in very clear weather, they will accordingly record details invisible to the human eye because of haze. *Courtesy Eastman Kodak.*

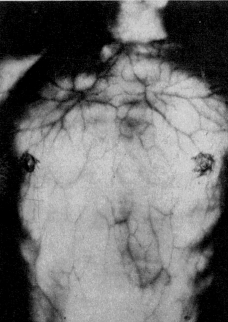

Plates 8 and 9. Infra-red radiation is frequently reflected or transmitted by coloured objects in a manner which has no connection with their visible colour. As a result obliterated, over-written and charred documents have been deciphered, and the presence of blood and other stains on dark materials demonstrated. The different infra-red reflective power of the inks and the charred paper enabled the record on the right to be made from the charred documents shown on the left. *Courtesy Eastman Kodak.*

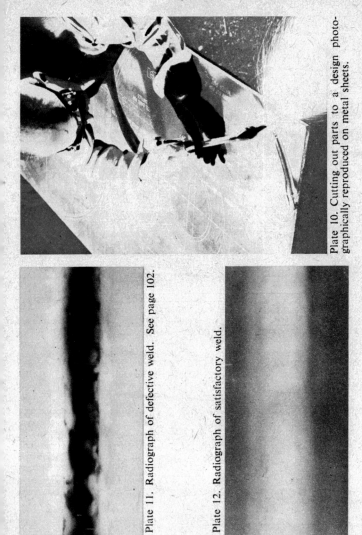

Plate 10. Cutting out parts to a design photographically reproduced on metal sheets.

Plate 11. Radiograph of defective weld. See page 102.

Plate 12. Radiograph of satisfactory weld.

Plates 13, 14 and 15. A natterjack toad eating an insect. The exposure times in each case was about a millionth of a second and was given by a 'Dawes' micro flash unit. This is triggered off by a weak electrical circuit which is completed when the moist tongue of the toad touches the insect resting on a weakly electrified plate. By introducing a very slight delay between the making of this contact and the firing of the flash, events taking place a very short time afterwards can also be recorded, as in the case of the insect halfway into the toad's mouth.

By courtesy of the Curator of Reptiles, London Zoological Gardens, and Kodak Research Laboratories.

Plate 16. A chameleon picking up an insect.

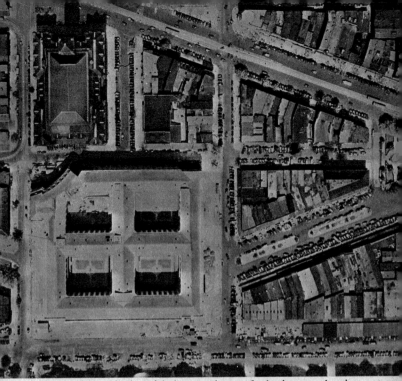

Plate 17. Low altitude aerial photographs are of value in town planning and in making traffic survey records at appropriate times of the day. The 'bird's eye view' provides evidence which could only be collected very laboriously from the ground. When photographs are made from fast-moving aircraft, exposures of the order of 1/300th second must be used. At low altitudes the image cast by the camera lens moves very rapidly across the focal plane. By arranging that during the exposure the film is automatically wound through the camera in the same direction and at about the same speed as this image, sharp pictures can be made even when the aircraft is travelling at 400 miles an hour. Compare page 107, par. 2. *Courtesy Eastman Kodak.*

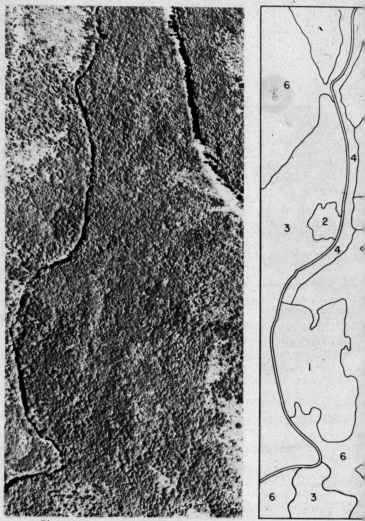

Plate 18. Comparative infra-red and Super-XX Pan photographs of the same Area of Forest. This technique enables certain types of conifer to be differentiated. The subtle differences are lost in photomechanical reproduction, but from the actual photographs the six types of tree are distinguishable as indicated on the key. *Courtesy of Harvard Forest and Fairchild Aerial Surveys, Inc.*

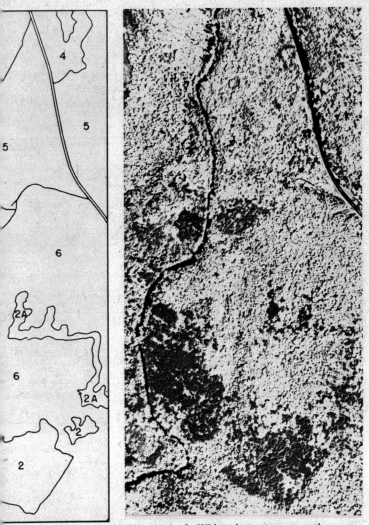

KEY: 1, White pine – old growth; 2, White pine – young growth; 2a, White pine indicating old fence row; 3, Mixed white pine, hemlock and hardwoods; 4, Hemlock; 5, Mixed hemlock and hardwoods; 6, Hardwoods.

Plate 19. Photograph for Determining Tree Heights by Parallax Measurements (see page 83). *R.C.A.F. Photograph.*

Plate 20. Geology: Fault North of Great Bear Lake. *Courtesy of W/C Pearce, O.B.E., Dr. A. W. Jolliffe and the R.C.A.F.*

Plate 21. Man's fight against land erosion (see page 86). *R.C.A.F. Photograph.*

Plate 22. Geology: Tertiary Strata near Cape Yakataga, Alaska – Oil-bearing strata have been revealed as a result of oil seepage, recorded in such photographs. *Courtesy Bradford Washburn.*

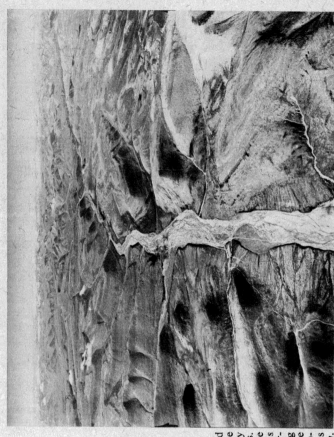

Plate 23. Typical Geological Field Photograph. In Britain the value of prospecting by air is limited by the extensive drift coverings. However, air photographs enable the British geologist to locate his exact position in featureless moorland and help an understanding of geological structure, while the value of a library of air photographs for teaching geology is world-wide. *R.C.A.F. Photograph.*

Plate 24. The bands of white
quartzite and grey sedimentaries
and lavas show up well on this
photograph of the Belcher
Islands, Hudson Bay. From such
aerial photographs, the geomor-
phologist can see the run of rock
strata immediately and thus
determine the likeliest areas for
field prospecting. A typical
example is the recent discovery of
valuable deposits of pegmatite
from the record of a dyke only
one foot wide discovered on such
photographs. *Courtesy of W/C
Pearce, Dr. A. W. Jolliffe &
R.C.A.F.*

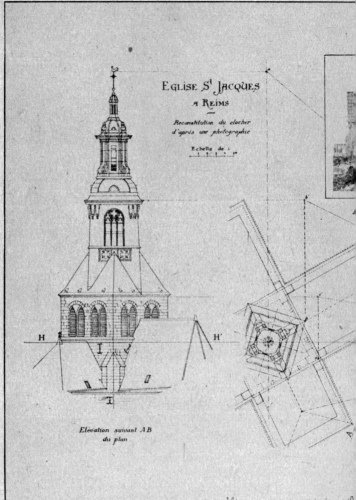

EGLISE ST JACQUES
A REIMS

*Reconstitution du clocher
d'après une photographie*

Echelle de :

H ——————————— H'

*Elévation suivant AB
du plan*

Pl. XXV

*Photographie d'avant-guerre
utilisée pour la reconstitution
du géomètral*

P. Deneux 1918

Plate 25. Production of dimensional plans from photographs. After the church had been destroyed (left) the essential dimensions were deduced from the pre-war snapshot (right). The task is greatly facilitated if the photographs are made under properly controlled conditions and, if necessary, facsimile replicas of such objects as the Elgin Marbles could be produced with the aid of properly-made stereoscopic photographs.

The science of deducing dimensions from photographs is called Photogrammetry. It was not until 1946 that Great Britain followed the example set long before the war by all the other major nations and established a University Chair in the subject.

Ordinary film base expands and contracts with changing humidity in a somewhat random fashion and until the introduction of 'Topographic' film base, negatives from which very accurate dimensions were to be deduced were made on glass plates. 'Topographic' film base has uniformly predictable and very low shrink characteristics, and is used in air survey work. If the prints are made on bromide paper laminated to aluminium foil, dimensional accuracy is retained in the print – from which it is usually more convenient to work.

(*Reproduced from 'La Metrophotographie appliquee a l'architecture' by courtesy of M. H. Deneux*).

Plate 26. Golf ball at the moment of impact. A high speed (electric spark) flash study. *Courtesy of H. E. Edgerton & K. J. Germeshausen.*

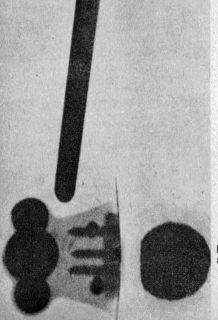

Plate 27. Radiograph of golf ball and club at the moment of impact, showing how the core is deformed.

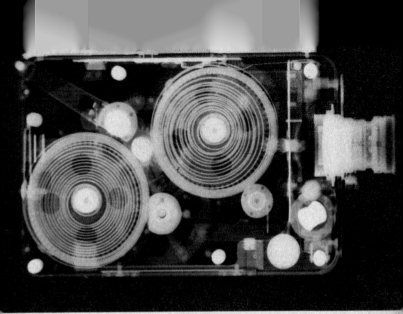

Plate 28. Radiograph of 16-mm. magazine Cine Kodak. *Eastman Kodak Company.*

Plate 29. Radiograph showing the path of the dirt particles in a vacuum sweeper while in operation. The bag is seen bottom right. *Westinghouse Electric International Co.*

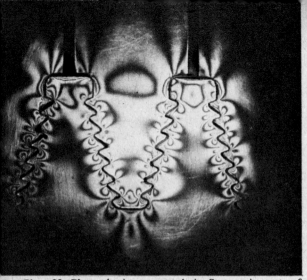

Plate 30. Photo-elastic stress analysis. Stresses in roots of turbine blades of a jet engine. (See the explanation on page 108.) *National Gas Turbine Establishment.*

Plate 31. Typical Metallurgical Photomicrograph. High chromium alloy cast iron x 100.

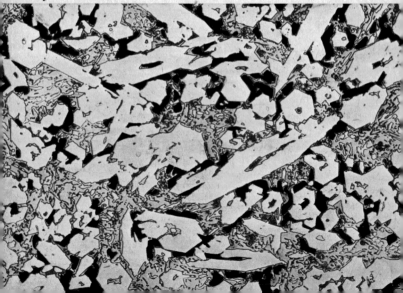

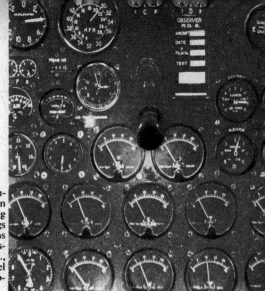

Plate 32. Typical Instrument panel as installed in a prototype aircraft during test flight. The readings given by the various forms of recording devices measuring strains, stresses, etc., are collected on one panel and recorded by a sub-standard cine camera.

Plate 33. Still from time-lapse cinemicrograph, showing cell-division in the sperm-mother cell of a grasshopper. This stage is the anaphase, taken while the chromosomes are separating into two groups. This photomicrograph of the living cell is made by the method of phase microscopy, at an approx. magnification of x 1,200. Phase contrast microscopy is a method by which local variations in refractive index or thickness of the specimen are shown up in the image as though these variations were brought about by differences in opacity. This enables a high contrast to be obtained in photographs of living cells, and details thus made visible which otherwise appear only in fixed and stained preparations. *From a film made in the Zeiss Laboratories, Jena, by Dr. Kurt Michel.*

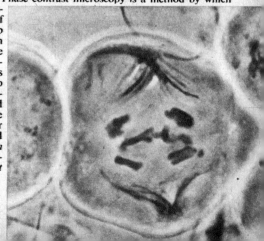

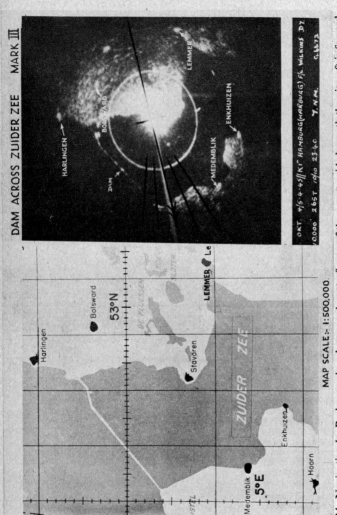

DAM ACROSS ZUIDER ZEE   MARK III

HARLINGEN →

DAM

BOLSWARD

LEMMER

MEDEMBLIK

ENKHUIZEN

OKT 4/5·4·43 || K⁺ HAMBURG(HARBURG) F/L WILKINS D7.
/0.000   2 65T   10/10 23·40   7 N.M.   G.4672

MAP SCALE:- 1:500,000

Harlingen

Bolsward

53°N

DE FLUESSEN

SLOTE

LEMMER   Le.

Stavoren

ZUIDER ZEE

Medemblik

Enkhuizen

5°E

Hoorn

IJSSEL

AMSTEL

34. Navigation by Radar-produced maps. A sort of map of the countryside beneath the aircraft is formed on the fluorescent screen of the Radar tube. Compare the image (as seen right) with a conventional map of the same area. Photographs of the screen were used to familiarise night flying navigators with the characteristic appearance of their targets on the radar screen. *Crown copyright.*

Plate 35. Prehistoric and Roman field systems and the post holes, storage pits and ditches of a succession of Iron Age and Roman settlements revealed as crop markings on fields of corn near Stanton Harcourt, Oxon. *Photo S. W. G. Allen, courtesy of Ashmolean Museum.*

Plate 36. Plan of Roman Villa, Ditchley, Oxon, revealed by crop markings. No sign of the villa or its surrounding walls and fields can be seen in the autumn when the land is ploughed.

Plate 37. Every spring the plan is outlined in growing crops, which locally are greener and stronger wherever the earth was disturbed nearly 2,000 years ago. *Courtesy of Ashmolean Museum.*

Plate 38. Hard cheese is made in a large vat rather like a bath. The milk is set with rennet into a junket and then cut up with special knives into small pieces about the size of a pea. The mixture of curd and whey is then stirred and the temperature gradually raised until the lumps of curd have exactly the right 'feel,' after which the heat is turned off and the lumps of curd are allowed to settle to the bottom of the vat.

The cheese maker is here seen testing the curd to find out if it is yet firm enough to settle. This judgment requires considerable skill and experience. *By permission of R.E.M.E. Magazine.*

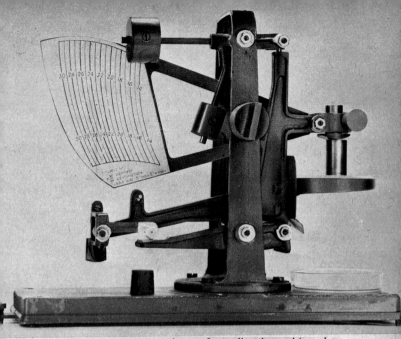

Plate 39. The correct consistency for settling the curd (see plate 38) still has to be decided on by the cheese-maker, but it is a great advantage to have an instrument which gives a figure for consistency so that no skill is required to find out whether the chosen consistency has yet been reached. Plate 39 shows an instrument for measuring the weight and height of a cylinder of curd, and also automatically calculating the density. The density (weight of a given volume) tells us how far the heavier whey has been able to run out of the curd to be replaced by lighter air. The firmer the curd the easier this process becomes. When the density has fallen to a previously chosen figure, the curd is settled. *Courtesy of Kraft Cheese Co.*

Plate 40. The grader tests the 'body' of cheese either by taking a cylindrical boring with the tool shown in the figure and judging the 'feel' of the plug of cheese in his fingers, or by pushing his thumb into the rind. But his thumb quickly tires and long training is needed to acquire the skill to give useful judgments in this way.

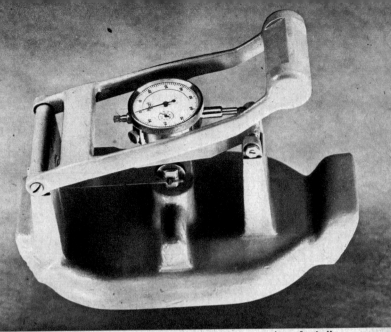

Plate 41. A hardness tester in which the penetration of a ball into the surface of the cheese under a standard load is measured. This serves as a kind of mechanical thumb and agrees fairly well with the grader's opinion. Keestra in Holland has made a similar study of the firmness of butter as judged by thumbing. *Courtesy of Kraft Cheese Co.*

Plates 42 and 43. Micromotion study of the Collation of Documents.
(See also page 107). The girl had small lamps strapped to her wrists so
that her hand movements in sorting papers could be recorded by long
exposure on one plate. Notice how much more economical of effort is
the arrangement in the lower picture.

Plate 44. The Flying Wing. The quest for the flying wing, an aircraft without fuselage or tail-plane, has at last succeeded. The Armstrong Whitworth tailless glider was constructed to provide data for a larger power-driven flying wing (see Plate 46). It is believed that this highly efficient aerodynamic form, for which a great future is envisaged, will lead to the simplified structure of aircraft of great strength. The glider, which carries a pilot and engineer-observer, has a wing span of 54 feet, wing area 443 square feet and total weight of 6,000 lb. *Photograph by Charles E. Brown.*

Plate 45. Photograph of a bullet moving at supersonic speed, showing shock waves emanating from the nose and other parts of the body, and also the turbulent wake. *Photograph by C. B. Daish.*

Plate 46. Britain's first jet-propelled 'flying wing,' the Armstrong-Whitworth A.W.52. Powered by two Rolls-Royce Derwent turbo-jets (seen in the centre of the photograph), it has a span of about 90 ft. The two-seater plane is a true all-wing design, except for the wing-tip rudders, the windscreen assembly and a slight bulge underneath. By doing away with the normal fuselage and tail unit and tucking everything inside the wing, drag and structural weight are greatly reduced.

able to act as the vitamin itself. Only a trial can determine
whether the new substance fits into the appropriate places
in the living cells well enough for it to take over the functions
of the vitamin, or only well enough for it to get in the way
of the vitamin. In some instances a chemical substance may
be able to act as a vitamin for one species while it is an anti-
vitamin for another species. Here are two examples. The
first concerns vitamin-B_6 or pyridoxine, one of the vitamins
that are sometimes classed together in the vitamin-B_2 complex. One derivative of this, desoxypyridoxine, can be used
instead of pyridoxine for the growth of certain bacteria,
whereas in the chick it acts as an anti-vitamin and causes

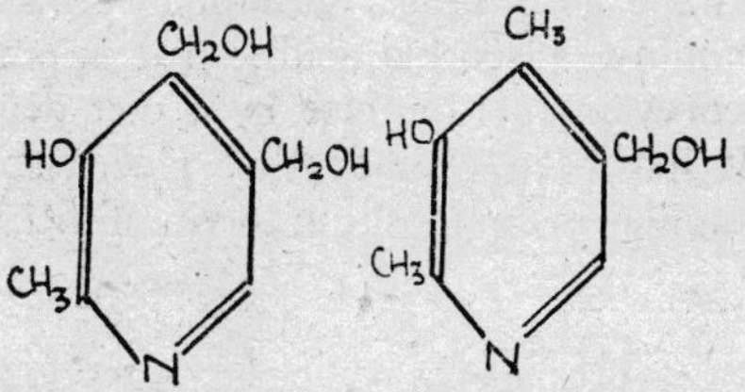

Pyridoxine.   *Desoxypyridoxine.*

Figure 10

deficiency of pyridoxine (Fig. 10). Another derivative is a
vitamin for some plants, for example tomatoes, and an
anti-vitamin for certain fungi. The second example concerns

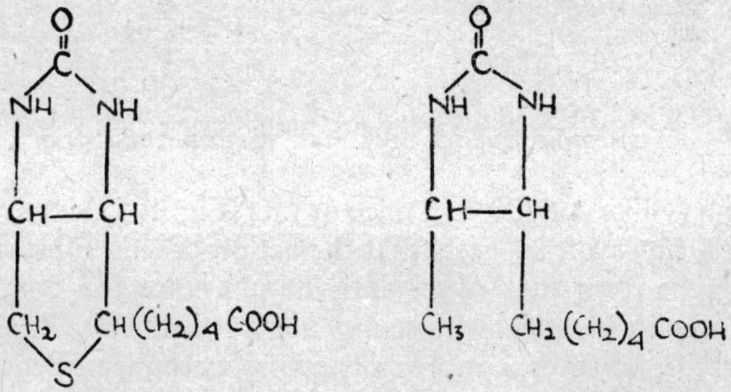

Biotin.   *Desthiobiotin.*

Figure 11

biotin, another vitamin of the vitamin-B$_2$ complex. A derivative of this, desthiobiotin, acts just as well as biotin in certain yeasts, but as an anti-vitamin in some species of bacteria (Fig. 11). In this instance, it has been found that the yeasts for which desthiobiotin can act as a vitamin have the property of converting it into biotin, whilst the bacteria for which desthiobiotin is an anti-vitamin cannot do this.

Artificial Vitamin Deficiency

Some animals normally do not require a particular vitamin in their food, since they are able to manufacture it themselves. For example, apart from humans and some of the higher apes and guinea-pigs, all animals are able to manufacture vitamin-C (ascorbic acid), so it is not possible to produce scurvy in rats or mice by a diet deficient in this vitamin. It has been claimed that glucoascorbic acid, a substance similar in composition to vitamin-C, will produce

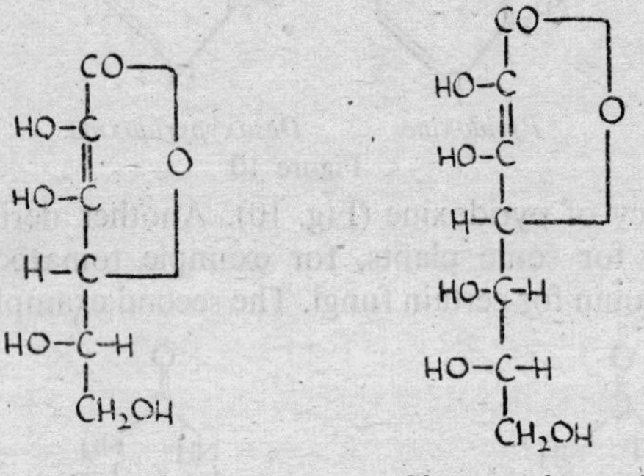

Ascorbic acid.   *Glucoascorbic acid.*

Figure 12

a scurvy-like condition in mice or rats (Fig. 12). More recent work, however, suggests that the action of this substance is different from that of an anti-vitamin since the condition is not quite identical with scurvy nor is it cured by vitamin-C. There is, however, a more satisfactory example of deficiency being produced in animals not normally requiring a particular vitamin. Mice are able to manufacture sufficient nicotinic acid for their requirements, whereas in man a dietary deficiency of this substance leads to the disease pellagra. It is possible, though, to produce deficiency in mice by feeding them with 3-acetylpyridine, a substance allied to

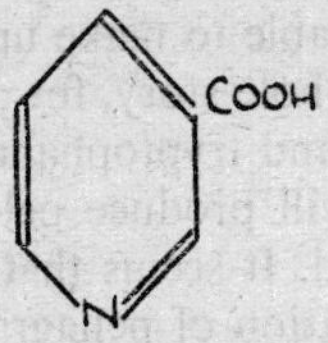

Nicotinic Acid. 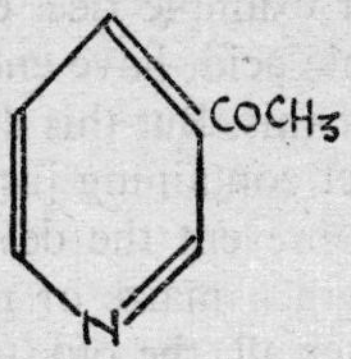   3-acetylpyridine.
Figure 13

nicotinic acid (Fig. 13). That this is a true anti-vitamin effect is shown by the fact that feeding nicotinic acid to the mice overcomes the deleterious action of the 3-acetylpyridine.

Pellagra

We might here consider in a little more detail some of the recent work on the causation of pellagra. This disease is widespread in the southern states of America, in parts of Africa and in the Far East, and is especially associated with the consumption of corn (maize). For a long time, it was thought that the disease was due to some toxin present in maize, but gradually it began to be looked upon as a vitamin-deficiency disease. In 1937, it was found that the disease could be considerably improved by nicotinic acid, although it often needed the administration of other vitamins which were lacking in the diet in order to produce a complete cure. Since then, methods have been perfected for the estimation of nicotinic acid in various foods, and it gradually became evident that the maize diets consumed by patients developing pellagra often contained more nicotinic acid than those diets containing no maize, which were consumed by many individuals who did not develop pellagra. Part of the explanation for this is that the body seems to be able to use an amino-acid, tryptophane, from which it can make nicotinic acid.

So the development of pellagra depends on whether there is
a deficiency of both of these substances in the diet. Maize is
known to be very deficient in tryptophane as well as fairly
deficient in nicotinic acid, whereas other diets, containing
for example rice, even though they may contain less nicotinic acid, have enough tryptophane to be able to make up
for this. But this does not seem to be the whole story, for a
diet containing just enough nicotinic acid and tryptophane
to prevent the development of pellagra, will produce pellagra if maize or maize products are added. It seems that,
after all, the old 'toxic' theory of the causation of pellagra
must have had at least some truth in it. Although we are not
yet certain what this toxic substance is, it is very likely to be
an anti-vitamin for nicotinic acid, and in fact recent work
suggests that it is indoleacetic acid (Fig. 14).

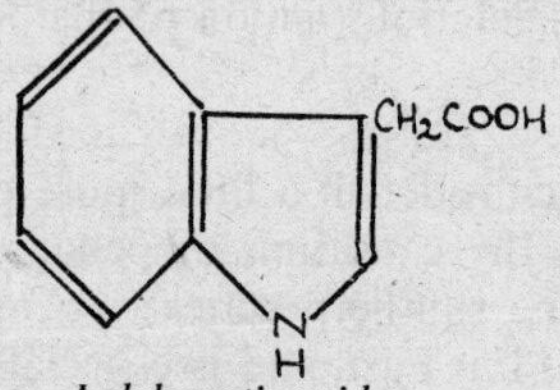

Indoleacetic acid.

Figure 14

Anti-Vitamin as Insecticide

Nicotinic acid is one more of the group of vitamins in the
vitamin-B_2 complex. Still another is inositol. Although this
has not been shown to be of much importance in the higher
animals, it is needed for the growth of some yeasts and, it
would seem, for some insects. And it is of interest in the
same sort of way that para-amino benzoic acid is of interest.
We noticed that the sulpha drugs act by 'starving' bacteria
of this substance, which, for them, is an essential nutrient.
Similarly, a substance is known which competes for inositol,
so that yeast will not grow in its presence unless a great deal
more inositol is added. You may not recognise this substance
by its name of γ-hexachlorocyclohexane, but 666 or gam-

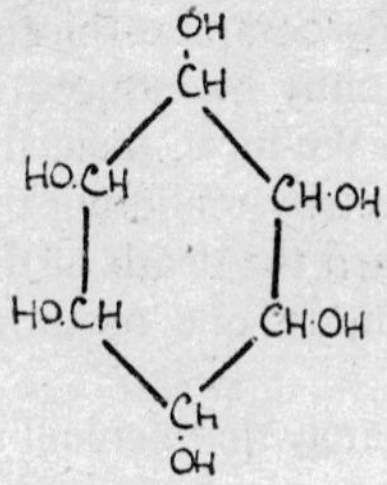

Inositol. 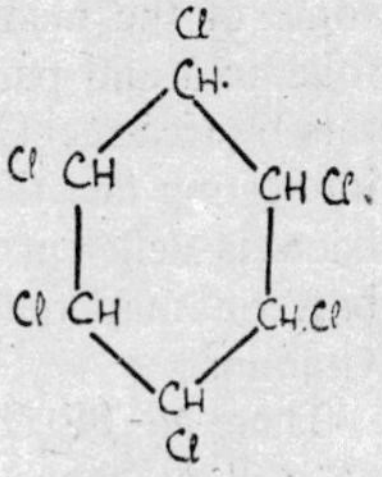   Gammexane.

Figure 15

mexane no doubt strikes a more familiar note (Fig. 15). It is a powerful insecticide and there is good reason to believe that it works as an anti-vitamin, starving insects of inositol so that they die of a vitamin deficiency disease.

Bacterial Anti-Vitamins

During the last few years, increasing evidence has accumulated that some vitamins are synthesised by bacteria in the alimentary canal of many animals. Appreciable amounts may be absorbed into the blood stream of the animal and decrease the dependence of the animal upon dietary sources of these vitamins. A curious result of this arises from the administration of anti-bacterial drugs, such as the sulpha drugs by mouth. This may cause a considerable decrease in the number of certain species of bacteria in the alimentary canal and consequently a decreased synthesis of vitamins. As a result, the amount of these vitamins in the diet, which was adequate when supplemented by the vitamins synthesised by the bacteria, may now not be adequate, and vitamin deficiency may be induced. This has been clearly demonstrated in experimental animals given sulpha drugs. In some instances, such as vitamin-K in rats, the amount of a vitamin synthesised by the alimentary bacteria makes it difficult to obtain deficient animals by dietary means alone, whereas the simultaneous administration of sulpha drugs leads to rapid and severe deficiency. Similarly, deficiency of some of the members of the vitamin-B_2 complex (biotin, folic acid and pantothenic acid) can rapidly be induced in rats by treatment with these substances. We have, then, the interesting fact that they exert their effect by rendering the bacteria deficient in a vitamin, and in turn the death of the bacteria may render their host deficient in one or more vitamins.

There has also been some suggestion lately that penicillin, as well as the sulpha drugs, may have a similar effect. Patients given penicillin by mouth seem sometimes to develop mild pellagra, and this would be due to the decreased formation and absorption of nicotinic acid, because of the killing of alimentary bacteria by the penicillin.

Quite apart from this indirect production of deficiency in the host the action of anti-vitamins on the bacteria is, of course, important in itself, as we have seen in the case of the sulpha drugs. The use of these chemotherapeutic drugs in medicine began some years before their mode of action was known, but now that we have this knowledge, a great impetus has been given to the search for new drugs. Large numbers of anti-vitamins have been synthesised in the hope that they will prevent the growth of harmful bacteria. It is, of course, necessary that these substances shall exert their effect to a far greater extent on the bacteria than on the infected host.

So far, it must be admitted that the search has not provided any spectacular results. However, some interesting developments have occurred and it seems likely that further work will provide something really worth while. One of the most promising lines of research is concerned with substances which antagonise pantothenic acid, still another vitamin of the B_2 complex. This is necessary for the growth of such bacteria as the streptococcus and the pneumococcus, the organisms which produce among other conditions blood poisoning and pneumonia. The most effective antagonist to pantothenic acid is pantoyl-taurine (Fig. 16). This

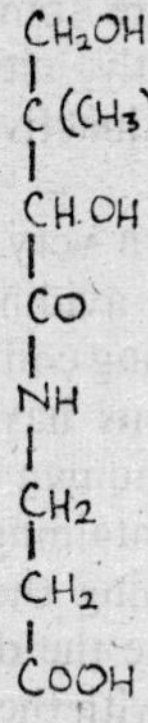

CH_2OH

$C(CH_3)_2$

$CH.OH$

CO

NH

CH_2

CH_2

$COOH$

Pantothenic acid.

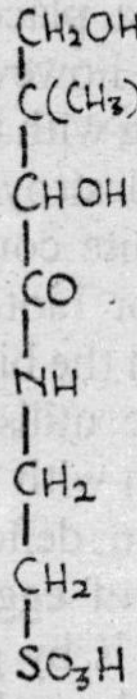

CH_2OH

$C(CH_3)_2$

$CH OH$

CO

NH

CH_2

CH_2

SO_3H

Pantoyl-taurine.

Figure 16

prevents the growth of several species of bacteria in laboratory cultures and will also prevent infection with these organisms in rats. Unfortunately, it is necessary to give far larger amounts of pantoyltaurine than could possibly be used in medicine, but it is likely that other derivatives of pantothenic acid may be more successful.

There is some evidence that the drugs which are used in the prevention and treatment of malaria – quinine, mepacrine, paludrine, and others – may act upon the malarial parasite in some such way as do the anti-vitamins. If this is confirmed, we shall have a new method of approach in the preparation of anti-malarial drugs. It has also been shown that anti-vitamins for pantothenic acid can cure experimental malaria in chicks. Again, this work is as yet not sufficiently developed to be applied in human malaria because it is necessary to use such amounts of the anti-vitamin as to produce deficiency in the chicks as well as in the parasites.

Anti-Vitamins which are not Competitive Inhibitors
So far, we have described substances which are chemically allied to the vitamins and act by competing with the vita-

mins for a place in the living cells. There are some anti-vitamins, however, which act quite differently, either by combining with the vitamin so that it becomes inactive or by actually destroying the vitamin.

Egg-white contains a substance which has a very strong affinity for biotin. This egg-white substance, avidin, combines with the biotin of the food and the resulting compound cannot be utilised by the animal. Experiments have been done both with laboratory animals and with human beings, and biotin deficiency produced by diets containing large amounts of egg-white. One way of overcoming the effect of avidin is by giving biotin anti-vitamins like the desthio-biotin we have described. These can combine with the avidin and leave enough biotin for the use of the animal. So we have the interesting situation that either avidin in egg-white, or synthetic anti-vitamins like desthiobiotin, will each produce biotin deficiency in an animal, but that both together may lead to normal healthy growth, since they combine with one another and leave the biotin itself free.

There are only a few examples of anti-vitamins which act by destruction of the vitamin. Breeders of silver foxes in the United States of America were much concerned a few years ago by the fact that some of the foxes on their farms lost their appetites, became very weak or even paralysed, and many eventually died. Investigation into the cause of this disease, which threatened serious financial consequences to many of the farmers, showed that it was due to deficiency of vitamin-B, (thiamine). It was then shown that this disease was associated with the consumption of raw fish which was often fed in considerable amount to the foxes. The raw fish contains an enzyme, thiaminase, which acts upon and destroys the vitamin in the food. Simple cooking of the fish was sufficient to prevent the disease since, like most enzymes, thiaminase is quite easily destroyed by the heat. A similar enzyme which destroys vitamin-C, is found in green vegetables, and this accounts for the instructions given by the Ministry of Food for the cooking of green vegetables. If they are put into cold water and gradually heated, especially if they have previously been cut up so that the enzyme and the vitamin in the cells are brought into close contact, quite an appreciable destruction of the vitamin occurs before the heat is sufficient to destroy the enzyme. On the other hand, if vegetables are put straight into boiling water, the enzyme is rapidly destroyed before it has had much time to act upon the vitamin-C.

This short account of anti-vitamins demonstrates three things. In the first place, the nutritionist has been able to make many advances in fundamental knowledge about the way in which vitamins act. He has also been able to produce experimental diseases for detailed study, in animals in which it had previously been difficult or impossible to produce them. He has, that is, a new technique at his disposal for the study of nutrition and, as with all experimental sciences, development of fundamental knowledge cannot proceed faster than the technical methods which are available.

Secondly, we now know that we must look, in our foods, not only for the presence of adequate supplies of vitamins but for the possible existence of substances which antagonise them. It is very unlikely that the anti-vitamins in raw fish or in maize are the only ones which exist, and it is necessary to bear in mind that there may well be others.

Thirdly, we have a completely new approach to the problem of the production of new chemotherapeutic agents whereby we can study the nutritional requirements of disease-producing bacteria, and then attempt to kill them by interfering with their nutrition by anti-vitamins. There is no doubt that, however laborious the search will be, and however numerous the compounds which have to be made, there will be sooner or later a number of effective new drugs which will give still more of that benefit to mankind which penicillin and the sulpha drugs have already given.

Modern Applications of Photography

D. A. SPENCER

USES OF AIR PHOTOGRAPHY

ALL our economists are agreed on one point, namely, that one of the most vital problems confronting the British people – a problem that must be solved if social security is not to remain a pipe-dream and the standard of living is to rise rather than fall – is to bring about a great increase in national efficiency by the raising of national productivity, both in volume and quality. I believe that photography in its many forms will be an indispensable tool in achieving this object.

Unfortunately, man is on the whole intellectually lazy, and it is a sad thought that only under the primitive stimulus of war does he usually muster the collective will and energy to apply available knowledge to achieve his aims in the shortest possible time. The major contributions photography made to victory depended not so much on basically new discoveries in the range of photographic technique as on the effective harnessing on an adequate scale of techniques whose potential value was known in 1939. This thesis is well exemplified by the recent history of air photography.

In 1940 a remarkable organisation was built up in Britain for collecting by air photography information about the day-to-day progress of our enemies' war effort. This organisation – the Photographic Reconnaissance Units and the Central Interpretation Unit – was responsible for obtaining the majority of the intelligence information we received from Occupied Europe after the fall of France.

When the Allies have got sufficiently tired of maintaining occupation armies in Germany it is to be expected that they will recall how successfully we kept an eye on Germany by the far cheaper and more convenient technique of photographic reconnaissance. In conjunction with a small group of specialists on the ground it is quite capable of ensuring that no major industrial or warlike activity takes place in Germany without our knowledge.

That aerial photographic reconnaissance would be an important source of information was, of course, recognised before the war, but few, even of those intimately concerned, realised before 1941 the remarkable results that could be obtained by a combination of first-class aerial photography with a thorough study of the resulting photographs by experts in many different fields working in close collaboration. The experience which has been gained is capable of direct application to peace-time research. Indeed, much information of interest in this connection is probably potentially available in the many thousands of negatives already made by the Allied air forces, and it is to be hoped that this will eventually become accessible through appropriate centralised libraries.

Interpretation

There are two main types of aerial photograph – the oblique, that is, the pictorial or bird's-eye view made through the side of the aircraft (Plate 23), and the vertical taken through the floor, producing a photograph of the ground as on a plan (Plate 1).

Although to the untrained observer the oblique presents the more familiar view, the scale varies from foreground to background and there is much 'dead' ground in hilly or wooded regions, and vertical photographs were of much greater use to our interpreters.

Such photographs are not pictures in the conventional sense, but rather a mosaic collection of details whose meaning is not immediately obvious. The amount of information which an interpreter can extract is directly proportional to his experience. This in turn is dependent on his full understanding of air photographs as a source of information, his knowledge of the subject being studied and his access to a series of photographs of the same area made on earlier occasions. He is immeasurably helped by the fact that the photographs can be viewed stereoscopically; that is, the picture appears to be a visual model in three dimensions. A right and left eye record is necessary for a scene to appear in relief, and the amount of this relief is determined by the distance apart of the two viewpoints. When we examine a scene with our eyes, which are only about a couple of inches apart, all sensation of relief disappears when objects are more than 500 feet away. But the interpreter examines the landscape as though he were a giant with eyes several hundred yards apart, merely by placing in his stereoscope a pair of prints from the series of overlapping records which the detached eye of the flying camera has provided.

Every stereo pair of war-time reconnaissance photographs was studied by specialists in many different fields, supplying its quota of information to each. By 1943, we had compiled what was virtually a photographic Lloyd's Register of enemy shipping, and we had learned to tell the type of cargoes and probable destination of every enemy ship that mattered. We followed every important aspect of German industrial activity and knew with remarkable accuracy the month-by-month output of all important factories. We watched Germany's progress in research on radar and atomic bombs. Photographic intelligence revealed enough information about the development of the flying bomb in time for us to make such preparations as were possible to reduce the attacks from a major disaster to a nuisance of no effect on the outcome of the war. Meanwhile, we were accumulating, *via* the air camera, essential information on every aspect of the Normandy beaches and landscape which would facilitate invasion.

Future Applications

We have accumulated, then, considerable experience with a powerful tool of research, and it remains for us to adapt it to the sane requirements of peace. A complete understanding of the various ways in which this is being done would require knowledge of the technique of photography which I must not assume. Accordingly, I shall have to ask the reader to accept some of my statements as to what is possible on trust, though I will illustrate them as well as I can by photographs showing the techniques in action. The fact that with one blink of its glass eye an air camera can make a detailed record of the countryside which it would take an artist months to draw is of course well known. What is not so obvious is the enormous importance of the fact that the record is an exact one from which sizes and distances can be accurately deduced. Much of the value of air photography in war and peace is due to the many ways in which such measurements can be turned to advantage. The most familiar, because the most obvious, is the use of air photographs in survey.

Surveying

The speed and convenience of aerial mapping has long been admitted, and for inaccessible or difficult country such as the jungles and swamps of Africa, aerial mapping is obviously invaluable, but its pre-war accuracy left something to be desired. As a result of war experience, it can safely be claimed that any required degree of accuracy is now attainable. In some cases, this accuracy exceeds that of conventional ground surveying, while the improved techniques available are resulting in appreciable saving in cost.

The usual procedure is for the aircraft to fly backwards and forwards over the territory to be mapped, taking vertical photographs on calibrated cameras – the dials of instruments recording height, tilt, etc., being photographed simultaneously along one edge of the film. The cameras employed are set to take photographs automatically at predetermined intervals, which are such that there is an overlap of about 60% between neighbouring records. This is necessary in order to provide the stereo records on which most mapping systems depend. Moreover, to ensure that gaps are not left in the record as a result of navigational errors, the parallel lines of flight are close enough together to ensure a generous overlap between each string of records. This lateral 'insurance' overlap, which is wasteful in time and material, is not necessary in the most modern air survey technique in which the navigation of the aircraft and the operation of the survey cameras is by radar control from a ground station. The pilot's responsibility is reduced to keeping his aircraft flying at the specified height along the radar beam, the camera operating at the correct intervals without his intervention. This technique also makes it possible for the ground station to direct the aircraft to any predetermined point on the terrain and then operate the camera as many times as are necessary to fill in any gap in the records of an earlier flight, due, for example, to the presence of an isolated cloud below the aircraft. As a result, two or three photographs are all that are necessary to cover such gaps, as against the many hundreds of exposures which are required to ensure proper coverage when navigation and photography are controlled by the aircraft crew.

The resulting photographs are built up into a mosaic record of the whole territory – a pictorial map adequate for many purposes and containing information from which dimensionally accurate maps can be prepared. The aerial camera in effect brings the territory to be mapped to the surveyor's laboratory for measurement.

It follows from the fact that by suitable techniques a contoured map of the countryside can be prepared that dimensioned plans of buildings can be derived from such photographs. From such plans accurately-scaled models can be prepared and rendered remarkably lifelike by sensitising their surface with photographic emulsion and then projection printing on to them from a negative of the target. The clockwork precision of the successful attack on St. Nazaire in March, 1942, owed much to the photographic-ally-produced model of the port which was made during the previous year. This model was photographed from various angles of approach and in lighting corresponding to that which would prevail at the time of the attack. Thus the participating forces were briefed with photographs of their various objectives which looked as though they had been made at ground level from a distance of a few hundred feet.

The technique of deducing the dimensions of a building from photographs was applied after the 1914-18 war to the problem of reconstructing war-damaged buildings of which dimensioned plans did not exist. Several French churches, for example, were rebuilt from accurately-scaled plans deduced from snapshots. Plate 25 is an illustration from Deneux's *La Metrophotographie appliquée à l'architecture*, a fascinating account of the geometrical methods available for carrying out the calculations.

In America at the moment, air photographic surveys are being carried out over all existing and several projected highways. It has been shown that it is possible to calculate from the photographs the cubic footage of earth to be removed or the concrete required at particular parts of the route far more simply and accurately than by ground methods, and the economy which has resulted is already regarded as having paid for the cost of the survey.

Air photographs made primarily for survey purposes will record a mass of data of interest to all those concerned with such economic aspects as land utilisation, agriculture, mining, town planning, electricity, water and transport services (see e.g. Plates 1, 18 and 17). In many cases, however, special flights at particular seasons and times of the day will be necessary if air photography is to contribute fully to developments in other fields, of which the following are representative examples.

Archæology

Archæologists were made aware through the pioneer work of Crawford, Kieller and Insall of the value of the point of view given by the aeroplane, and many sites of archæological importance have been discovered by its use. Slight banks, grass-covered foundations or depressions in the earth's surface which are all that remain of early earthworks, may pass unnoticed on the ground, but acquire significance when viewed from such a distance that any shadow cast forms a geometrical pattern which is obviously man-made. Such shadow sites will be most clearly revealed when the sun is low and in the right direction to cast a significant shadow. However, the most fascinating – because quite unsuspected – phenomenon which air photography revealed was that growing vegetation is affected as regards its average size and colour by the previous history of the soil. For example, if a ditch has been dug on a chalk down and afterwards ploughed flat and sown with corn, for ever afterwards the silt filling that ditch differs from the ancient, never disturbed soil. The more moist or more fertile silt promotes the growth and deepens the colour of the crop and hence in the spring the ancient excavation is annually outlined by a patch of darker green corn (Plates 36 and 37).

Ancient roadways and wall foundations are sometimes revealed by the reverse effect. The shallow stony soil of the site results in a relatively poorer growth of the crop, or during a drought leads to more rapid 'parching' of vegetation on the site (Plate 35).

A remarkable example is the ground plan of Caistor, near Norwich (Venta Icenorum). The roads, streets, houses, temples and market places of this Roman town are all clearly revealed in an air photograph made during the drought of 1928. It will be a matter of chance whether such crop markings will record on air photographs made for other purposes, and for maximum results specially arranged flights under the direction of an archæologist must be made over areas, known to be of interest, at appropriate seasons and times. A recent series of flights planned in this way, in two days' flying time, added more to our knowledge of Roman Britain than the previous two centuries of archæological research !

Ecology

Ecologists, concerned as they are with what might be termed biological geography, have already used air photographic surveys of South America to provide data on the density and distribution of population, distribution of arable land, natural barriers and natural avenues of travel, sources of power, fuel and water, land utilisation, facilities for transport and the influence of topography on the location of roads and towns. Such investigations have a close relationship to the sort of studies we have made of Germany during the war, while the methods so successfully applied to ferreting out the activities of our human enemies are directly applicable to non-human pests – animal and vegetable. The control of such disease-carrying insects as the mosquito and the tsetse fly by spraying from the air is now familiar. More indirect methods of control may well emerge from studies of bird migration and population on inaccessible islands made by means of the air camera. As a minimum, surveys of this type should be a very convenient method of checking the efficiency of our attacks on such pests as the boll weevil or the Colorado beetle. Meanwhile, the advance of bracken over grassland, and of prickly pear in Australia, and the distribution and effect on each other of plant communities (woodlands, jungles, prairies) are already being effectively studied by air photography.

Colour Filter Techniques

So far I have dealt with ordinary black and white photographs of the type one can make with the photographic films used for amateur snapshots, but made through a medium yellow filter. This absorbs ultra-violet radiation and deep blue light which, being scattered by haze, would otherwise reduce the clarity of long-distance photographs. Full advantage has yet to be taken of the fact that, by the use of specially sensitised films and suitable colour filters, the camera record can be made to emphasise detail and differentiate between various features of the landscape in a manner quite impossible to the human eye. Forestry provides a number of simple illustrations. Thus, a recent air survey of the forests of Southern Sweden was made at a season when the beech foliage contrasted with that of other trees – enabling the beechwood resources to be assessed. This is a simple case, however, for, to the eye and the ordinary photographic film, beech foliage is noticeably lighter than the general run of leaves.

By employing over the camera lens a filter which transmits only the particular part of the spectrum reflected most freely by the foliage being studied, it is possible to exaggerate in the photograph subtle colour differences which would be undetectable on an ordinary photograph.

An extreme example of this technique is the use of films made sensitive to invisible infra-red radiation. Infra-red photographs differentiate coniferous trees very strongly from deciduous – the latter recording as though their foliage was white (Plate 18).

An interesting war-time application of such colour filter techniques was the determination of the depths of off-shore water along enemy coast lines.* If a beach is photographed vertically from the air a fair amount of underwater detail is recorded. This means that we are photographing the sea-bed through the overlying water. Now red light is more rapidly absorbed than green light during passage through greenish sea water. If therefore we take two photographs – one through a green filter and one through a red filter – the relative blackening on the two photographs which is determined by the amount of light reaching the film will be greater in the case of the green filter photograph and the magnitude of the difference will depend on the thickness of the overlying water. By careful measurement of these relative blacknesses it is therefore possible to calculate the actual depth of the water down to depths of 40 feet. Such information was invaluable in planning landings on enemy coasts and has

* Devised by the Army Air Photography Research Branch at Larkhill.

already found one peace-time application in oceanography.

Marine biologists are using it for making surveys of animal communities such as oyster beds and seaweed concentrations (for instance, plates 4 and 5). In its present form it has potential value in the preparation of navigation charts, control of pollution, erosion, and the study of the effect of currents and tides on the formation and movements of sand bars. When sufficiently refined, it has been suggested that the method might even be capable of distinguishing between the differing bodies of sea water whose movements determine the movements of fish shoals. The shoals themselves could almost certainly be detected by appropriate forms of reconnaissance photography – an innovation which would have obvious economic importance.

Forestry

These, however, are possible future applications of colour-filter techniques where the records must be made under properly controlled conditions if they are to prove of real worth, and, as I have already indicated, their present use is mainly in forestry studies. Here, even qualitative techniques have already proved of real value. Thus Canadian foresters, from aerial photographic surveys of forest land, have obtained, in addition to such obvious data as the types and density of trees, details of the composition, age and structure which are invaluable in forest control. From the photographs, type maps can be prepared which speed up, simplify and cheapen the operations of forest management. By measurements on stereoscopic pairs of photographs (of the type of plate 19) the height of the timber can be determined by simple instruments. Air photographs are also used in fire control, planning, evaluation of damage by insects, location of property lines, relocation of Canadian highways and the planning of new ones.

It is frequently suggested that colour photography from the air would simplify the task of interpreting such photographs, and already it is known that in some cases useful information not obtainable from black and white photographs can be recorded on colour film. Insufficient experiments have so far been made, however, to draw any but the most general conclusions.

An aerial colour photograph is easier to interpret by the unskilled, but it is possible that only in certain special cases will it be of important assistance to the skilled interpreter.

During the war a limited amount of 'Aero Reversal Kodacolor' was used by the British and American Air Forces. This was an integral tripack film which yielded subtractive colour transparencies built up from inseparable yellow, magenta and blue-green dye images (see article on Colour Photography in *Science News* 3). Its main application was for such specialised purposes as recording the coloured identification pattern of the target indicator flares dropped by the Pathfinders during night raids and the recording of underwater obstacles near landing beaches in the Pacific.

In a modified form of this film one of the sensitive layers consisted of an infra-red emulsion and the three layers were processed in colours which were not necessarily complementary to their colour sensitivity – as is required for a 'natural' colour rendering. In consequence, green grass, for example, might appear magenta in the colour transparency and features in the landscape which in a normal colour photograph might escape detection could often be clearly differentiated in this 'camouflage detection' film. Such material has potential peace-time applications in forestry, but more objective research is required to evaluate statistically the relative advantages of such specialised forms and natural colour as against black and white air photography, for it is easier than might be thought to be the case, for a skilled interpreter to distinguish between different types of vegetation in black and white air photographs.

Geology

In some regions, vegetation is zoned with respect to elevation, inclination of slopes, proximity of water and rock outcrops, and hence provides a guide to the interpretation of topographic features, some of which – such as the site of old beaches – are obscure on the ground.

Changes in vegetation over a period of time are often associated with important topographic processes, and as the surveys spread to such vegetation types as sphagnum bog and submerged seaweed beds, they impinge on the interests of geologists, for they yield indirect data on such problems as the silting of estuaries, coast erosion and other factors controlling the development of scenery.

The geologist is, in any event, already aware of the value of air photography in simplifying his studies of geological structure and land forms. Thus, the size, shape, distribution and evolution of complex sand dunes is much easier to assess from the air. Air photographs made for such purposes will in turn facilitate the work of prospectors for mineral deposits, and the mining engineer (see e.g. plates 22 and 24). In Canada, for example, the information on the distribution of rock formations furnished by the early geologists was mostly confined to the main water routes and did not help in the case of wide areas distant from the principal rivers. It is estimated that only 11% of Canada has so far been adequately mapped from this point of view, and that without the use of air photography it would take 200 years to complete the task at the present rate of progress. However, the Canadians are now going all out on an air survey programme, and during 1946 a basic photographic coverage of about half-a-million square miles was obtained – about one-seventh of the total area. For 1947 the target is another three-quarters of a million square miles. Already this work has paid a dividend in the discovery from the photographs of rich tantalite deposits.

Soil Erosion

One of the earliest and most characteristic features of the growth of a civilisation is the change which is imposed on the vegetation of the countryside. Where Nature would have a forest – or, as in the case of the Nile Valley, a desert – man makes fields, and so on. When, as in England, the country is small and the civilisation old, one finds that the landscape is eventually almost entirely man-made. With increasing facilities for making such modifications which the twentieth century has placed in his hands, man runs grave risks of upsetting the balance of Nature to his own detriment – as when he creates huge deserts in America by unwise deforestation. The new deserts in turn facilitate the production of disastrous floods which, among other things, may lead to the transfer of alluvial soil to inconvenient regions.

Accordingly, extensive development of land by empirical methods will sooner or later have to give way to controlled development based on a study of conditions which can conveniently be made from the air. Since the natural vegetation over any particular region is a product of the various geological and climatic attributes of that region, its study before any development is planned can lead to a rational exploitation of virgin land and appropriate modifications to our treatment of land which is being misused.

Already over 50% of the U.S.A. has been photographed from the air to enable the Soil Conservation Service of Washington, D.C., to compile an inventory of the physical land factors involved in soil erosion. These photographs (Plate 21) are used to determine soil type, land slope, gradient, present use and degree of erosion. The records not only provide a factual bird's-eye view of the land and its present condition, but will be invaluable in future years as a basis for comparing land conditions from time to time and for following trends in land use. The acreage of crops and other vegetation can be determined very rapidly and economically by colouring the photographic prints according to the crop, cutting up the prints and weighing the collection of various-shaped pieces of any one colour. The area can be determined from this weight with an accuracy of 1 in 1,000. Such photographs can also supply a basis for the making of payments to farmers for diverting acreages from soil-depleting to soil-conserving crops, and for carrying out approved soil building practices.

Physics

The photographs we have been considering were all made from aircraft flying at heights of not more than a mile or so, and the physicist is, on the whole, only mildly interested in them for the data they provide on atmospheric haze. The physicist is more interested in the records obtained on photographic plates which have recently been sent into the stratosphere in rockets. He has thus obtained records of cosmic radiation and the sun's spectrum made above the absorbing blanket of the atmosphere. The man in the street is more impressed when automatic cameras installed in such rockets primarily for other purposes bring back from 100 miles up photographs of the earth's surface which demonstrate conclusively that the earth is a ball. However, the data on cosmic radiation will, in the long run, be a far more important contribution to our control over Nature than spectacular confirmations of something known to Galileo.

The Future

Unfortunately, many of the most interesting peace-time applications of air photography have no immediate commercial future, and the problem is therefore how to get such work carried out. The British Ecological Society has taken a first step by circulating to scientific authorities and responsible Government departments a memorandum recommending the establishment of an aerial unit for scientific work. Such a unit would form an invaluable focal point for researches in many fields and would be of great potential value in another connection. Photographically speaking, we were very backward in air photographic techniques at the beginning of the recent war. Photography was not highly regarded as a service career and certainly offered few attractions to the scientifically-trained young minds on which research largely depends. The question is therefore how to keep alive this interest in the minds of intelligent men, who doubt whether the next war will be anything like the last one and who are averse to wasting their creative energy on the devising of techniques which may not be required. The creation of aerial units for scientific work, operating from the principal armed forces' air photographic research establishments would seem a reasonable solution, if any group of investigators faced with a scientific problem which air photographs might help to solve could, through appropriate mechanisms, have access to such units. The ground technicians would then have a worthwhile interest in devising modified equipment and techniques for the solution of many different types of problem.

There would be real satisfaction in being a member of a team whose work involved helping, through an archæological group, to uncover details of our history; helping, under the guidance of physicists, to clear up the mystery of cosmic radiation; fighting with the geologists against soil erosion and with the ecologists against the ravages of pests; and so on. Devising techniques most suitable for each type of investigation would result in the accumulation of experience and a nucleus of the right type of trained research worker and technician. It would follow that, if there is another war, photography from the air will be ready from the word 'go' to play its part in man's next effort at destroying what is left of his civilisation.

SOME APPLICATIONS IN INDUSTRY

Broadly speaking, photography is of value in commerce and industry because it can:

(1) make records which are permanent sources of reference and exact measurement in a variety of convenient forms;

(2) operate efficiently under conditions where the eye is helpless either because the light available is too high

or too low in intensity, because the event is too transient or too protracted to see, or because visible light is
not involved at all;

(3) record movement, if necessary in such a way that the
time scale is altered;

(4) play a basic part in certain fabrication processes;

(5) facilitate all aspects of training and education.

Records

Let us dismiss with a mention such obvious applications as
the choosing of factory sites by aerial survey, the recording
of each stage in the erection of buildings and plant and the
photographic printing processes – known as blue print and
diazotype – by which the plans for such activities are dupli-
cated. A conventional photo-copy of a plan made by these
processes is the same size as the original and only minor
improvements in the processes themselves have taken place
in the last 20 years. Document copying processes in which
enlargements or reductions are possible, however, are growing rapidly in importance. In these processes the original is
photographed by various forms of specialised camera on to
bromide paper, photographic film or plates. In the mere fact
that the photographic record can be made smaller than the
original we have the subject-matter for a long book, for new
applications arise almost daily.

In the Statfile system, engineers' drawings are reduced to
$6\frac{1}{2}$ inch by $4\frac{3}{4}$ inch records on non-inflammable film. In this
form an enormous bulk of drawings can be filed in a
relatively small space and at a standard size. From the
negative, copies on paper to any required dimensions can
be produced by conventional enlargement. In addition, there
are numerous systems for recording documents on 35 mm.
or 16 mm. film with correspondingly greater saving of space.
These range from primitive adaptations of conventional
miniature camera equipment to specially designed fully
automatic machines which can be operated by people with
no knowledge of photographic technique.

During the war essential information about every member of the armed forces was recorded on 35 mm. film, in the first instance to simplify keeping pay records, etc., up to date. However, the same technique obviously facilitated the sending of information on other subjects from one theatre of war to another. A specialised aspect of this so-called microgram service, namely, the Airgraph scheme – a direct descendant of Dagron's pigeon post from beleaguered Paris – made one advantage of such micro-records obvious to the general public, who received and sent more than 1,000 million Airgraph and V-mail letters during the war. The original letters were photographed on to 16 mm. film for convenience of overseas transport, and bromide print enlargements made at the receiving end for dispatch by surface mail.

The release and saving of valuable storage space, protecting of irreplaceable records against loss by war, accident or theft, and the increased availability are obvious advantages of micro-records, of which banks and big business houses are making growing use. U.S. public documents can now by law be thrown away if miniature film copies exist. One machine tool firm which had nearly half-a-million drawings occupying 1,500 square feet of floor space has now microfiled the lot in two drawers of a letter file. Libraries, which began by storing the contents of newspapers in this way, are now extending the method to their books. All English books in the British Museum written before A.D. 1500 have been recorded in this way, and the Library of Congress offers a service of microfilms or positive enlargements of any part of its ten million volumes. Such reproductions serve the student just as well as the, often irreplaceable, originals. This technique has also been suggested as a means of dealing with the problem of publishing and distributing those scientific papers which are too specialised or transient in interest to justify printing in full in the ordinary scientific journals.

Specialised machines – of which the Recordak is a typical

example – have mechanised the procedure for transforming huge piles of documents into midget records on microfilm to a point where the equipment can take its place side by side with other 'business efficiency' aids such as accounting machines and office duplicators. In the latest model of the Recordak, for example, documents such as cheques need only to be fed into a slot by the operator. When they emerge a few seconds later both sides of the document have been recorded next to each other on 16 mm. film. Many documents are recorded in this way, at a rate of 1,000 per hour if necessary, purely as a safeguard against loss or fraud – for example, the cheques passing through a banker's clearing house or the incoming entries complete with serial number and date in football pool and bookmakers' offices. In such cases systems are available for finding automatically particular records on the negatives. For smaller users combination units are available which both make the microfilm record and project it for reading purposes.

Increasing attention is also being given to mechanising the production of paper prints from these negatives, and war-time developments in high-speed automatic processing are a promising first step in this direction. Thus the U.S. Navy required positive photographic records of the images produced on the fluorescent screen of radar cathode ray tubes in the shortest possible time: the right-hand side of plate 34 shows the kind of picture. The problem was solved by producing a photographic film which could be processed to a positive image in a matter of seconds in a processing machine which applied hot solutions to the film in rapid succession. Each solution was removed in turn by vacuum suction and permanent records of the changing images on the radarscope could be seen twelve seconds after photography.

In America hot-processed motion pictures have already been used experimentally as a source of television 'originals' of news events. The overall time for complete processing and drying a single frame of the 16 mm. used was 45 seconds as against 40 minutes for the normal procedure, and the processing machine operated at the rate of 8 feet per minute.

The R.A.F. asked for a photographic paper which could be printed in contact with an unwashed negative and dried in a minimum of time, and here again the problem was successfully solved.

By combining these two techniques, suitably-designed machines would make it possible to produce a large number of copies of a document in a matter of seconds if this was required. A fully automatic machine of this type would of course be an expensive piece of equipment, and small organisations are more likely to be interested in the various improved forms of reflex copying systems. In making a reflex copy of a document a sheet of thin photographic paper is pressed into contact with the document to be copied and this is then exposed to light through the back of the sensitized paper. The difference in the amount of light reflected by the dark and light portions of the original document is utilised to form the photographic image. Upon development, a negative image is obtained from which any number of positive prints can be made.

Crude reflex copies can be made with ordinary photographic paper of high contrast. For best results special forms of so-called reflex bromide paper and specially-designed printing frames are recommended as a simple method of obtaining copies of documents at a cost of a few pence per square foot and minimum capital outlay.

Quality of Raw Materials

Turning from business to industrial efficiency, let us glance first of all at photographic tools which are helping to control the quality of raw materials. Most of these tools originated in research laboratories, because scientific research is based on efforts to reduce phenomena to forms that can be seen and measured. The powers of exact description provided by photography are the very foundation of precise knowledge and make it natural to use appropriate types of photographic material as the retina of microscopes, telescopes, spectroscopes, oscilloscopes, stroboscopes, stereoscopes and X-ray tubes, converting them into recording instruments infinitely more versatile than the human eye.

Using these instruments enables us to reveal and record layer by layer the composition, structure and characteristics of materials. Starting at the outside, a beam of electrons, if suitably reflected from the surface on to a photographic plate, produces a diffraction pattern which reveals the arrangement of the atoms in the outermost layer of the reflecting body – of importance in the study of lubrication, polishing processes and other surface phenomena.

Photomicrography normally records the surface as the eye sees it. By sending a beam of electrons through thin layers of material an electron image of objects far smaller than can be seen by optical instruments can be recorded photographically. X-rays, when suitably reflected from surfaces, form diffraction patterns on photographic plates which will reveal the architecture of the molecular structure of matter to a depth of a few hundred atoms. X-ray micrography, in which X-rays transmitted by layers a few fractions of a millimetre thick are recorded on fine-grain photographic emulsions, yields radiographs which when studied under the microscope will settle such questions as whether the copper in a copper-aluminium alloy is in solid solution or not. Infra-red photography will penetrate thin crusts of rust and reveal, for example, the cause of porosity in tin-plating.

The now familiar radiographic and gamma ray techniques enable flaws and faults to be recorded even though they are embedded in the centre of steel a foot thick.   Plates 11 and 12 illustrate how X-rays can show up the faults in a welded metal junction. Finally, the Betatron, which generates 20-million-volt X-rays, is extending this non-destructive probing for faults into even greater thicknesses of metal.

Some of these techniques are still in the laboratory stage. Others have already been harnessed as industrial tools as a result of the development of apparatus which can safely be placed in the hands of people almost ignorant of physics. Of these techniques, let me illustrate three.

Spectrographic Analysis

The conventional method of determining the composition of materials is by chemical analysis, and this is still the most reliable method in the case of non-metals. The engineer's main raw materials are, however, metals, and in particular alloys, and here photography in conjunction with the spectroscope has freed hundreds of people from the boredom of routine analyses, for it yields, in a few minutes and at a fraction of the cost, results which would otherwise involve hours of laborious work. Spectrographic analysis as a technique was handed over to industry almost ready-made by astronomers who had perfected it in their efforts to determine the composition of the stars. Industrial spectrographic analysis is based on the fact that when elements are heated in, for example, an electric arc, they emit characteristic line spectra. In a mixture of substances the intensities of the lines of the various elements, as recorded on the photographic plate of the spectrograph, are related to each other in a way which depends on the percentage present.

Both qualitative and quantitative analysis of a minute particle of a substance is therefore possible in the few minutes necessary to expose and process a photographic plate and measure the densities obtained with a micro-densitometer.

Absolute methods of quantitative analysis in which the densities of the lines are interpreted directly as percentages are not yet reliable for a variety of reasons. On the other hand, the majority of routine works analysis is performed to keep a check on the uniformity of a product. Accordingly, specimens of accurately known and qualitatively similar composition are used as standards for the production of graphs from which the analysis is read off direct, the spectrum of these comparison standards being recorded for reference alongside that of the sample to be analysed. In this way very high accuracy can be achieved by a purely routine procedure. It so happens that the 'sensitive lines' of metals (i.e., those which are in evidence when only minute quantities are present) lie between 2,000 and 10,000 Å., and are therefore accessible with a quartz spectrograph working in air and recordable only by photography. The sensitive lines of most non-metals are of wavelengths shorter than 1,850 Å., and here a vacuum spectrograph – a more expensive instrument – is required. Accordingly, although the economy in time and material with which spectrographic analysis can be carried out suggests that it may eventually replace the majority of routine chemical analytical control, as yet its chief industrial application has been metallurgy. The application of the method to the control of the composition of alloys has been one of the outstanding developments in the non-ferrous metal industry during the past ten years. Refining operations can be followed step by step, and many firms now control their foundry output by this method. In the case of alloys, the reference standards referred to above must have a known history, since the intensity of the lines in an alloy spectrum may vary according to whether the samples are in the as-cast state, the wrought state or in the heat-treated condition.

The working procedure has been reduced to a simple routine by the design of apparatus requiring a minimum of adjustments in use, and specially devised photographic plates whose characteristics facilitate the easy interpretation of the records.

Metallography

From the engineer's point of view the correct chemical composition of a structural material is, however, only half the battle. It may still be useless for his purpose if the constituents are not properly combined or the material is non-homogenous. Unless, therefore, the engineer knows his material literally inside and out he must play for safety in designing castings, struts, and so on, compensating for ignorance in this respect by undesirable dead weight. This is costly, and, in such machines as the modern aeroplane, impracticable.

Fortunately, in the case of metal alloys a thorough examination of the surface layers of properly chosen specimens will provide much valuable information about the metallurgical structure of the material.

The photographic examination of the surface of metals is called metallography. Such mechanical properties as hardness and ductility are related to the microstructure of metals and alloys, and numerous defects are directly attributable to abnormalities in this structure, which is built up of a mass of interlocking crystals. Accordingly, one of the main objectives of the metallographer is to obtain photo-micrographs of polished and etched metal surfaces, recording the nature and size of the individual crystals as in plate 29. Recording their change in size and nature with heat treatment, cold working and fatigue has helped to explain the basis of these phenomena and – more important – helped to bring them under the metallurgist's control.

Photography of the macrostructure, i.e., the structure as seen by the eye, not only helps in the selection of significant areas for photomicrography, but provides a record of markings indicative of unsoundness, cracking, segregation, and other faults.

The distribution of particles of sulphide in steel provides a clue to the process of crystallisation and can be recorded on the photographic emulsion without the use of a camera, simply by placing a sheet of bromide paper soaked in dilute sulphuric acid in contact with the polished surface of the specimen. Hydrogen sulphide is liberated locally by reaction between the sulphides and acid, and this in turn reacts with the silver halide in the photographic paper, forming a dark silver sulphide image.

X-ray Crystallography
X-ray crystallography is another typical example of the

development of a research into a works tool. This is a
technique which reveals the molecular architecture of crystals by a study of the patterns produced when narrow wave-
bands of X-rays are diffracted during their passage through
the material. The atoms of solid substances are always
arranged in a characteristic manner which determine the
physical properties of the material in bulk. The various
patterns produced by diffraction by parallel layers of atoms
are characteristic of these various geometrical groupings.
The first interpretation of these spectra requires of course
an expert physicist, but from the point of view of non-
destructive testing the method can be used in a variety of
ways by workers who need no more knowledge of the physics of the subject than the average owner of a wireless set
has of the physics of radio. The interpretation of patterns
produced by a modern industrial X-ray crystallographic
unit is, in their hands, not so much in terms of crystalline
structure as on such broad but informative lines as variations
in heat treatment, corrosion, cold rolling, annealing and
residual stresses. It is interesting to note that a 'picture' of
a molecule showing the arrangement of the atoms in space
can be made by working back from these diffraction data.
A series of masks is made consisting of opaque bands whose
widths and orientations are calculated from the diffraction
records. Successive exposures on a single sheet of photographic paper are made through these masks and the super-
imposed record shows the spatial arrangement of the atoms
in the molecule. This method eliminates the laborious calculations inherent in indirect methods of determining molecular structure from X-ray diffraction data, and the physicist's picture of a molecule which results is identical with
that previously deduced from chemical evidence.

Fabrication Processes

Turning now to fabrication processes, perhaps the most
potentially valuable development will be the wider application of a photographic technique which shortened by months

the period between the design stage and the first flight of the later types of aircraft. This is the so-called photo-template system. A template is a copy or pattern of some part of a mechanical structure. It is usually flat, made of metal or wood and carries construction details of the particular part which assist the fabrication and assembly of machinery or equipment.

Templates have been used since the beginning of the nineteenth century and some of the more elaborate modern forms require as many as 400 man-hours to draw out. Moreover, the laborious scribing operations involved have often to be carried out as many as half a dozen times. It has frequently been pointed out that a tremendous amount of time could be saved and risk of dimensional errors eliminated if these subsequent drawings were reproduced on the metal by photography. It was, however, the special combination of circumstances arising in mass production of war-planes that brought about practical development of this idea. A modern aircraft contains as many as 25,000 parts, whose outline at some stage had to be drawn on metal with an accuracy measured in thousandths of an inch. The design serves as a guide when the sheet is cut, filed, drilled or punched to make the aircraft part itself or the tools with which such parts are made. For the precision inspection and assembly of components, accurately made check template and assembly jigs are required, all produced from the same basic drawings. The high degree of precision essential, the complexity of the designs, the frequent modifications as design progressed, the need to ensure exact interchangeability of parts made in different aircraft plants and the vital need for speed resulted in the photographic reproduction technique becoming thoroughly established in American aircraft plants. Months of time and many thousands of pounds were saved on each design, and it seems certain that such methods will find peace-time applications in other engineering industries.

In a typical photo-template technique the design is scribed

once and for all on lacquered aluminium sheets. These are placed on suction copyboards and photographed down on to glass plates, using precision cameras of the process-engraving type. The negatives are then projected in the same apparatus on to sheets of aluminium sensitised with photographic emulsion (Plate 10).

The big advantage of this projection system is that the scale can be altered when required – for example, to allow for different degrees of shrinkage when the metal from which a part is to be made is changed, or when preparing small models for wind tunnel or other forms of examination. The projection process is, however, relatively costly to instal, for precision equipment is essential if the photographic image is to reproduce the original within the tolerances of typical specifications.

For small parts where no change in scale is involved a simpler and cheaper method is to make a reflex copy of the full-size drawing on a glass photographic plate and then print the negative down on to a metal sheet coated with a light-sensitive emulsion. Alternatively, the original drawing can be made on a translucent coating on plate glass and contact negatives made from this are then printed directly on to the sensitised metal. However produced, the metal prints are then cut out and become the templates or patterns that go to the shops.

It is claimed that photographic template methods have saved as much as £5,000 in building prototype aircraft and shortened the time between designing and test flight by from two to four months as a result of the reduction of time required to turn out patterns for shop fabrication. So far, only the aircraft industry has made any serious attempt to exploit the process. It would, however, seem immediately adaptable to motor-car and boat-building, even if only to facilitate the work involved in making mock-ups, i.e., full-scale models in wood, by photographically reproducing the original layout directly on the wood, which the builder would use immediately without the delay of marking out.

Photo-mechanical Processes

Photographic prints on metal are the basis of another major industry – photo-lithography – and here again war-time researches have made possible considerable simplifications in the working procedures. Thus the rapid production of maps in the field was facilitated by the preparation of zinc plates coated with photographic emulsion on to which negatives could be projection-printed. A simple processing technique resulted in litho printing plates ready for use. Although this technique simplified printing plate production it did not cheapen it, and further development of this technique may well be of greater interest to business houses who already employ simplified photo-litho methods for preparing their own literature rather than to litho printers as such.

The introduction of so-called 'coloured contact screens' which eliminate the necessity for skilled hand work in reproducing half-tone illustrations is however an important advance. These screens may well represent the most important improvement in the half-tone process since the introduction of the ruled screen itself. They enable the contrast of the final printing plate to be adjusted to that of the original as a result of making controlled variations in the colour of the printing light, and at the same time they automatically yield a much closer approach to accurate tone production than can be achieved by the conventional half-tone process.

A typical photomechanical printing plate is in effect a photograph in metal, and by making the original drawing a suitable design it became possible to make exceedingly delicate metal devices – such as the grids of valves or the hair-line resistances known as strain gauges – by stripping the metal photograph off its temporary glass support.

Sometimes, as in the thousands of hair-line graticules which were used in gun sights, the metal image is left on its glass support. By using substantially grainless photographic emulsions the lines on such graticules were quite free from graininess and could, when necessary, be made so thin that as many as 1,200 separate lines could be produced in each millimetre width.

Quality of the Product

Radiography. – The war also led to a considerable increase in the use of photographic methods for examining fabricated articles. The most important of these was radiography – the recording of X-ray images on photographic film or paper.

X-ray pictures are essentially shadowgraphs made by placing the object to be examined between the X-ray tube and a fluorescent screen or a light-tight cassette containing photographic film. The image which is seen on the screen or recorded on the film is produced by differential absorption of the radiation during its passage through the specimen and when articles made of light metal and of low economic value are to be examined as manufacturing routine, visual inspection of the image is the usual practice. Examination of the core of golf balls, flash lamp cells, or of the electrode assembly of small radio valves are typical examples. The method is also useful for the inspection of lower-grade light alloy castings. The photographic method is, however, essential for dense materials, for the examination of fine detail and where records are required to meet a specification. Typical examples are the checking of the proper alignment of the inner components of sparking plugs, shell fuses, torpedoes, electrical condenser units and vacuum pumps. In some cases visual and photographic inspection is profitably combined. Thus the centering of the core of a heavily-insulated cable can be viewed at right angles as the cable is drawn behind the fluorescent screen. On seeing a suspected region, the operator throws a switch, thus making a radiograph and marking the region in question on the casing.

During the development stage of an assembly, X-rays will help to demonstrate why a device fails to function, examples being the revealing of the presence of drops of solder which may cause short circuits, or, in the case of a Bourdon gauge, interfere with the hidden moving member.

The value of X-rays as an inspection tool has been clear since Röntgen made the first half-dozen radiographs some 45 years ago, for five of these were typical of the subjects now examined by the industrial radiographer. The early industrial applications of X-rays were, however, attempted with adaptations of apparatus primarily designed for medical work, and it was only when equipment specially designed for industrial use appeared that radiography came to be regarded as an essential engineering technique.

Typical industrial equipment is mobile and can be applied to structures in situ. It thus becomes possible to determine the position of concealed wiring and plumbing, determine the general character of the reinforcement in old concrete floors to be used for supporting new machinery or check telephone poles in the highways for unsound wood. Repeat radiographs of old timber will show whether death-watch larvæ are alive by recording any change in their position. These are more or less specialised applications, however, and it is in the foundry and welding shop that X-ray equipment has become imperative.

It is now quite common for specifications to demand radiographs of welds and castings, for X-rays will demonstrate the presence of cracks, blow-holes and slag or sand inclusions which might otherwise be revealed only after expensive machining, or remain as an undetected menace to the soundness of structures on which our lives may depend. Not only does radiography reduce machining costs by keeping unsound parts from the production line but, by showing the nature and location of irregularities, it indicates methods of avoiding them, thus increasing the yield from such raw materials as castings. Because radiography enables soundness to be assessed it often permits the use of lower cost materials and fabrication methods, as when sand castings are substituted for forgings or spot welding for slower rivetting. Accordingly, no high-pressure welded boiler receives a Lloyds' Class I certificate unless radiographs of every weld are forthcoming, and every light alloy casting used in aircraft construction is first submitted to X-ray examination. The thickness of metal which can be penetrated is directly related to the kilovoltage of the X-ray set, and a modern portable industrial unit employing 400 kilovolts will penetrate up to 5 inches of steel. For thicker or inaccessible specimens gamma rays are employed.

Gamma Radiography

Whereas the wavelengths of X-rays are approximately one hundred thousand times smaller than those of visible light, gamma rays are nearly one million times shorter, and we have to employ one million volts to generate them by the technique used to produce X-rays.

Radium is a natural source of gamma radiation, and a radium bomb – that is, a tiny fragment of a radium salt enclosed in a platinum capsule in a protective lead cylinder – is all the equipment required. Exposures of the order of several hours are given by removing a lead plug in the cylinder, and radiographs through 8 inches of steel are possible. Radon, which permits an even smaller source of high gamma-ray intensity, is to some extent replacing radium in industrial radiography. It is highly probable that artificial radioactive elements will also be employed for this purpose in the future.

X-ray equipment has been devised which will yield gamma rays. An example is the Betatron, which is essentially a specialised form of transformer in which the secondary consists of electrons rotating in a ring-shaped vacuum tube. At a certain point in the alternating current cycle an additional high voltage pulse is applied to the primary, causing the electron orbit to expand. The electrons in consequence strike a platinum target, producing million-volt X-rays which will penetrate 20 inches of steel – a thickness far beyond that economically practical by other means.

High-speed Radiography

For the majority of industrial work, an exposure of seconds

is of little consequence, but a new type X-ray tube permits radiographs to be made with exposures of 1/500,000th second. The tube is so designed that currents of the order of 2,000 amp. can be passed through it as a result of condenser discharge, and radiography of rapidly-moving enclosed machine parts, such as pistons or the impeller blades of turbines, has become practical.

The silhouette photograph of a golf ball at the moment of impact aroused admiration a few years ago, and we had hardly recovered from the surprise created by Edgerton's substitution of a fully-detailed photograph for this silhouette when with this new technique we obtained a record of how the inner core of a ball behaved at the critical instant (Plates 26 and 27).

Let us now turn to techniques of value in assessing the performance of machines and in search into new designs.

High-speed Photography

One of the earliest triumphs of applied photography was the freezing of the image of events lasting minute fractions of a second, thus permitting their study at leisure. The subject was illuminated by an intense flash of light produced by the discharge of an electrical condenser across a spark gap. Various types of circuit have been devised, some of which yield a flash shorter than one millionth of a second.

In a convenient modern light source the discharge takes place across a gas-filled tube yielding a flash of intensity equal to 50,000 40-watt bulbs with an effective photographic duration of about 1/30,000 second. The tube has a life of well over 5,000 flashes. Typical of the engineering applications of such equipment is the photography of an aeroplane propeller revolving at high speed and determination of the amount of distortion during rotation by making measurements on the photograph. Plates 13 to 16 show how this kind of work can reveal the very rapid feeding movements made by some animals.

Flashlight technique of this type permits the use of an

ordinary camera. When, however, the subject is luminous, specialised forms of camera are necessary. Thus, in studying the propagation rate of burning explosives, photographic film has been attached to drums driven at right angles to the direction of flame travel and so caused the flame to draw graphs which enable the changing speed of the explosion wave to be measured. Spinning mirrors have been used to move the image of such flames over a stationary photographic plate and so record the life history of explosions lasting minute fractions of a second.

I suppose the most photographed event in history was the atomic bomb explosion at Bikini. Five hundred cameras of many different types were employed and more than 100,000 still pictures and three million feet of cine-film were exposed during the two tests. Much of the data on the potential destructive force of these bombs will be based on these records.

High-speed Cinematography

It is obvious that a cine-film record is a valuable way of analysing a movement. For many purposes an ordinary cine-camera used at normal speed is quite adequate. Very often, however, it is not convenient to photograph the actual movement itself. When the movements are too small they can be magnified by the use of a follower connected to a suitable dial gauge which is photographed. When they are too complicated, numerous or inconvenient to record directly, as in the analysis of the performance of an aircraft in flight, dials and cathode ray tube screens which record such data as air speed, altitude, bank and stresses and strains in various parts of the machine can all be collected on one panel which is recorded by a normal speed cine-camera (Plate 32).

New fields are opened up when the camera is speeded up. Phenomena whose life history is too short-lived to be examined by the unaided eye acquire a new significance when the time scale is altered by slow motion (high speed) cinematography. Details of displacement and distortion of objects in rapid motion are directly observable as a function of time when the film is projected at normal speeds, while velocities and accelerations can be calculated from frame-by-frame measurements.

Typical engineering applications are the observations of oscillations or surges in valve springs, the hunting of synchronous motors, the functioning of telephone relays, clutches, ringers and dials; coin-collecting mechanisms; contact conditions and the arcing of switches at make-break. It has proved of value in studying such diverse problems as the behaviour of high-speed loom shuttles and observations of warp breakages, the melting of fuse wire during a burnout and the detection of gas leakage around the charge in a gun when fired. It has been applied to the testing of materials in connection with impact testing, stress analysis and bending moment, and to the reduction of noise in such apparatus as typewriters and accounting machines. Valuable studies from the design point of view have also been made on such relatively slow-moving machines as milling machines and punch and hydraulic presses. Thus it will reveal erratic operations caused by excessive deflections and clearances, and information relating to punch and die adjustment and to the flow of metal during punching operations.

If the movement to be studied is rotary or rhythmical, it is well known that it can be apparently slowed down by viewing the subject by stroboscopic light of appropriate frequency. A typical example is the study of the flow of air through a fan blade, smoke being fed into the air stream to make the air currents visible. In such cases the record can, of course, be made in an ordinary camera, but the method is of limited application. Genuine ultra-speed cinematography demands radical redesigning of the camera itself, because the film must rush through the camera at about a mile a minute, a speed which effectively rules out the possibility of its normal method of progression – alternate stops and starts.

A laboratory type makes use of an argon-filled discharge tube capable of flashing from 1,000 to 5,000 times per second. No shutter is used on the camera since each flash lasts only 1/250,000th second, and the film does not move appreciably during this period.

In commercial ultra-speed cameras, moving optical devices are built into the camera which send the images formed by the lens streaming along in synchronism with the rush of the film. Thus, for a very brief time, as the film and image flow together, each image is stationary with respect to the film. Perhaps the simplest camera of this type is the Eastman High Speed camera which uses a rotating glass block. Although this camera can record up to 3,000 pictures per second, 1,000 pictures per second is adequate for the study of most machine parts. Naturally, instruments of this type are fairly costly, and since the majority of engineering firms could only find occasional use for them, it is usual for them to hire the equipment, together with a trained operator as and when required.

Cine-records of the movements made by workers engaged on repetition jobs can be analysed in a similar manner in order to determine the most efficient and least tiring sequence of operations. As an example, a step-by-step analysis of a timed cine-record of a girl sorting spools led to the devising of a method which increased her output 80%. The sorters find the new method less tiring and, being paid on an output basis, everyone profits by the change.

It has been suggested that making such records on infra-red sensitive film would have the psychological advantage that the worker would not be disturbed by the obvious presence of a flood of additional lighting which is necessary when ordinary cine-film is exposed in typical workshops. The recent spectacular increase in the working speed of infra-red emulsions makes such a proposal quite feasible.

For the so-called 'micro-motion study' of repetition movements a cine-record is not necessary. Instead, small lamps can be attached to the moving parts of the operator's body,

their light being then recorded over one cycle of the operation by working in a dimly lit room while the camera shutter
is left open. If the lamps are made to flash at a uniform rate,
the speed of the operator's movements can be calculated as
well as their path. When two hands are employed – as in
the case illustrated in Plate 42, saw-tooth modulations of
different types can be employed in each lamp to facilitate
sorting out on the photograph of the movements made by
each. The figure shows a girl collating the sheets of a manu-
script. The movements made by her hands along the desk
are revealed by the intermittent light trace. The greater
smoothness of movements, speed and economy of effort
resulting from a rearrangement of the positions of the
various piles of paper is seen in Plate 43. Messrs. W. H.
Smith used this technique to study the movements made by
a typist in making out invoices. This led to a rearrangement
of the data on the form, which reduced the time of typing
each form by two-thirds.

Here again, by working in a room lit with fluorescent
light – which contains no infra-red radiation – the lamps
attached to the worker's wrists can be covered by visually
opaque infra-red transmitting filters and the record made
on an infra-red emulsion. This adaptation of a war-devel-
oped technique used in training the pilots of night fighters
has the advantage that the operator can work under normal
illumination conditions and with a minimum of distraction
due to the presence on her wrists of the recording lamps.

Photoelastic Analysis

Many faults in the operation of machines are due to stresses
whose existence it is impractical to predict at the design
stage. Valuable guidance can, however, often be obtained
by the technique of photoelastic analysis.

A scale model is made of the object to be tested, using a
suitable transparent material. Loads proportional to those
acting on the real object are applied to the model, which is
then examined by polarised light. An unstrained model

placed between crossed Polaroid screens appears uniformly black under these conditions. Whenever stresses occur, however, the refractive index of the material is altered and bright lines will appear which contour the principal stresses, providing valuable information as to the internal conditions of a similar shaped metal object under similar conditions of load (Plate 30).

If the model is made of a thermo-setting plastic the stress pattern can be rendered permanent by heating the model while it is under load. It can then be cut apart for three-dimensional stress analysis. Calculation of the stresses in all such cases involves measurement of the distribution of the pattern, and this is materially simplified by making these measurements from photographic records – particularly when the stresses are dynamic in moving parts. Here, a cine-film record is the only practical way of assembling the data in measurable form.

Conclusion

This review has been an attempt to demonstrate how certain photographic techniques originating in research laboratories have so far contributed to industrial efficiency.

New ways of harnessing photography as a research tool are constantly being devised, for its powers of exact description are the very foundation of exact knowledge.

It was Eddington who suggested that all that could ever be known of Nature consisted in essence of pointer readings. Certainly the scientific research worker nearly always takes pains to arrange his experiments so that the final observation employs the sense of sight, and the ways in which photography can be used to produce records for visual inspection is limited only by the ingenuity of the worker. Its value for recording invisible radiations is obvious, but even when the eye might appear to be an easier or quicker means of making a record, the camera is often a convenient tool for eliminating drudgery and ensuring accuracy, as when it watches dials, counts dust particles, records pressures, and so on.

Tiny pulsations due to subtle faults in machines can be recorded and enlarged until not only is their presence demonstrated, but measurements which reveal their cause become possible. The differences of refractive index in the laminæ of hot and cold air produced by stringing heated wires across a wind tunnel can be recorded and intensified so that even air currents may be photographed.

In many cases, such as the movement of the light spot on the cathode ray oscillograph, the human eye can only see the movement as a blur of light and the moving photographic film is an essential tool for reducing the record to intelligible form. In others, as in the transient tracks produced in cloud chambers by subatomic particles, photography is the only way in which a record can be made for subsequent interpretation and measurement. When the disintegrating atom is embedded in a photographic emulsion the tracks made by its debris of charged particles are produced by direct action on the silver salts. Measurement of these tracks made permanent by development enables the energy and momentum of the various particles to be determined, thus providing the vital key to the interpretation of the atomic explosion (see plate 31 in *Science News* 5). It can therefore safely be claimed that but for photography our hopes of harnessing atomic energy would remain a novelist's pipe-dream.

I think it will be obvious that many of the techniques described are highly specialised and can only operate at maximum efficiency when the behaviour of photographic materials under a wide variety of conditions is properly understood and catered for. It is therefore a matter of regret that as yet not one of our leading universities has established either a teaching course or a research department on Photography. In Germany, before the war, nine universities offered training and facilities of the type required, in Japan two and in Italy four, to refer to our late enemies alone. In England such courses as are available are intended primarily for professional photographers; and those enterprising industrialists who wish to make use of this twentieth-century tool for solving one of their twentieth-century problems must as yet rely on their own resources, or the technical service departments of the photographic manufacturers, for essential guidance on photography as a record-maker in the widest sense.

However, a committee appointed by the Royal Photographic Society has recommended the establishment of a readership in Photography within a British university. Such a course would be a valuable first step in ensuring a supply of thoroughly competent workers of the type required if we are to take full advantage of this potential contribution to our industrial efficiency.

This article is based on two of the Cantor Lectures on Photography which the Author gave to the Royal Society of Arts in March, 1947.

Mathematical Instruments and Calculating Machines

DR GABRIELE RABEL

WHO are ENIAC, EDVAC and EDSAC?

If you think they are old Anglo-Saxon kings from the days of 1066 and all that, your guess is wrong. ENIAC is an Electronic Numerical Integrator and Calculator, and EDVAC and EDSAC are persons of a similar character.* ENIAC and EDVAC are of American parentage, EDSAC is English, a native of Cambridge. Their remote ancestor is Calculus who, surprisingly, was a simple pebble. Thracians, we are told, set aside dark calculi to count their dark days and white calculi to add up the happy ones. Another ancestor is Abacus, a board on whose drawn lines (or rods or wires) counters are pushed along. One form embraces Heaven and Earth, earthly beads counting as one unit, heavenly beads as five.

No improvement of mathematical machinery is reported before Napier's Bones (1617) which were a kind of movable multiplication table. The seventeenth century is characterised by vigorous endeavours to 'rationalise' mathematical practice, relieving the worker from mechanical repetitive procedure to free his mind for real thinking. One approach to this goal was to simplify the *language* of mathematics through various systems of notation and the symbolical calculus as devised by Vieta, Descartes, Newton and Leibniz. Another path to the same goal was the relegation of all mechanical work to machinery. In 1642, Pascal built the

* DV stands for Discrete Variable, and DS for Delayed Storage. E always means Electronic, A Automatic, and C Calculator. The ENIAC has been in use for some time, the other machines are still *in statu nascendi*.

Arithmometer and, inspired by this addition machine, Leibniz made a better one. He is also said to have constructed an algebraical machine for the solving of equations.

In the early 19th century, a young mathematics professor in Cambridge, Charles Babbage, dedicated his life to the idea of saving the time and brains of mathematicians by means of mechanical aids. He devised two types of machines, which he called Difference Engine and Analytical Engine.

The Difference Engine is based on an arithmetical law which appears to the layman almost miraculous. If we form the squares of the numbers 1, 2, 3, 4 etc., we get the series 1, 4, 9, 16, 25, 36, 49 ... and find that the differences between them are 3, 5, 7, 9, 11, 13 .. so that the differences of the second order are constant$=2$. The first differences of the cubes 1, 8, 27, 64, 125 ... are: 7, 19, 37, 61 ... the second differences: 12, 18, 24 ... so that the differences of the third order are again constant$=6$. Somewhere the differences of any such sequence seem to become constant, and this gave Babbage the idea that one can build up tables by adding differences. His Difference Engine was to compute any kind of tables (e.g. of logarithms and trigonometrical functions) both more quickly and more correctly than was possible before. But the machine remained unfinished for lack of funds, and for the same reason the Analytical Engine could not even be begun – which is a great pity, for it was designed in full detail and meant to be a 'General Purpose Machine' like the ENIAC.

The mechanical aids to mathematics are of two distinctly different types which Professor Hartree distinguishes as 'Mathematical Instruments' and 'Calculating Machines,' while the American engineers call them 'Analogue' and 'Digital' machines. It is essential to understand what constitutes the difference between them.

Two mathematical instruments, the Slide Rule and the Planimeter, are widely known. The purpose of the planimeter is to find the area of a figure encompassed by a given curve. If a pointer connected to a wheel is made to follow this curve, its sideways movements combined with the revolutions of the wheel make it possible to read off the area under the curve. Mathematically one finds the area of a rectangle by multiplying width and height. If a figure has an irregular contour, one can divide it into a great number of narrow rectangles and sum up these small strips. If the strips are supposed to be infinitesimally narrow and their number infinitesimally great, the summation is called integration and the rough-hewn sign for a sum Σ mellows into the more elegant yet widely dreaded sign $\int$ which denotes an integral. The planimeter achieves mechanically what integration achieves mathematically. The figures submitted to the planimeter are often symbols for physical quantities, e.g. the indicator diagram which measures the efficiency of a steam engine. Otherwise the curve may represent any mathematical function whatever. Some of the most complicated instruments called Integraph, Integrator or Differential Analyser may be roughly described as one planimeter working on top of another. One integraph uses optical methods. It measures very small and irregular areas by the amount of light they transmit. Another much-used type of 'Analogue' is the Electrical Model, especially handy for the solution of flow problems. To find the distribution of the current in an extended network by computation implies the solution of a great number of linear equations; it is easier to build a model of the network adjusted to the given conditions and to carry out simple measurements. Such an electrical model can be used for networks of any kind, because the laws of flow are similar for electric charges, gases, water, steam or heat, and it is simpler to insert an ammeter into an electric circuit than, say, a flow meter into a pipeline.

These few examples suffice to illustrate the principle of a mathematical instrument or Analogue. Numerical data are not used directly for computation, but translated into physical quantities. In the slide rule, numbers are represented by lengths, in the planimeter by lengths and areas, in the electrical models by amperes, ohms and volts. We might perform a simple multiplication such as 13 × 0.74 by using the formula Voltage=Current × Resistance. If we send through a resistance of 13 Ohms a current of 0.74 Ampere, we may read from the voltmeter the product 9.62 Volts.

But obviously the result is burdened with all the inaccuracies of measuring instruments and there is a limit of accuracy even for the finest instrument.

The situation is completely different in digital machines. They deal with numbers as such and usually count some discrete events, e.g. electrical signals. They cannot, like the Analogues, handle continuously varying quantities; if asked to solve differential equations, they must confine themselves to summation and cannot pass on to integration. But their accuracy, not depending on physical measurements, is the same for the 10th or 20th decimal as for the first.

It is not the purpose of this article to describe any one machine fully. I have only tried to clear up, first for myself, then for others, the elementary principles of such contrivances. This, I found, can best be done by reverting to the first modern calculating machine as sketched by Babbage a century ago. At that time the Jacquard Loom had just been invented and its punched card method was eagerly seized upon by Babbage. He writes: 'The Jacquard loom weaves any design which the imagination of man can conceive. The patterns designed by artists are punched by a special machine in sets of pasteboard cards and when these cards are placed within the loom, it will weave the desired pattern – either as a damask cloth if warp and weft are of the same colour, or using different colours.' 'The analogy of the Analytical Engine with this well-known process is nearly perfect. The Engine consists of two parts: (1) the Store in which the variable to be operated upon and the results of operations are placed; (2) the Mill into which the quantities are brought to be operated upon. Every formula which the Engine can be required to compute consists of algebraical operations to be performed upon given letters and of modifications depending on the numerical values assigned to these letters. There are therefore two sets of cards, the first to direct the nature of the operations, the other to direct the particular variables on which those cards are required to operate ... The Engine is of the most general nature. Whatever formula it is requested to develop, the law of its development must be communicated by two sets of cards.' Some professor inquired what the machine could do, if in the midst of algebraical operations it was required to use logarithms or trigonometrical functions. Babbage answered that the machine might compute the desired numerical values in the shortest possible time, but that it might also use punched card tables. 'Suppose the engine required the logarithm of a given number, it will stop, ring a bell and ask for it. Thanks to the configuration of holes, only the right logarithm will fit the given number. If the attendant has brought the wrong card, the Engine will ring a louder bell.' Babbage adds: 'It will be an interesting question which time only can solve whether tables on cards will ever be required, for the computations made by the Engine are so rapid that it may make shorter work by computing direct from formulae.'

The problem is not solved yet. The ENIAC uses ready-made tables, another American machine does not. And concerning a 'punched card memory' Professor Hartree reasons that 'though it greatly increases the power and range of the machine, it does so at the expense of the speed and fully automatic character of the work.' It is still true that cards require human attendance, and humans are so slow!

One of Babbage's greatest worries was the carrying over of the tens. In principle the problem was solved by Leibniz' toothed 'stepping-up wheel' which, when passing from 9 to 0, moved another wheel by one tenth. But what troubled Babbage was the time required for the carriage. 'I concluded that nothing but teaching the Engine to foresee and then act upon that foresight could achieve an unlimited number of carriages in one unit of time.' He actually succeeded in devising a mechanism by which all the movements the carriages required when adding two ten-digit numbers were made at once instead of successively, and he estimated that, if the velocity of the moving parts were forty feet per minute, one addition or subtraction could be completed in one second.

The ENIAC completes 5,000 additions in one second. The punching system for giving instructions and for registering results is still in use, a card reader scans the punched cards and electrical contacts are made through the holes. Thus the card data are conveyed to the 'Constant Transmitter' which makes them, in the form of electrical signals, available to other units. Babbage's two sets of cards are supplanted by two sets of communication lines – programme lines transmitting pulse groups which represent instructions, and digit lines transmitting pulse groups which represent numbers. Further all the thirty ENIAC units are permanently connected to a third set of lines which supplies a standard pattern of pulses from the Cycling Unit. This contains an oscillator which runs at 100,000 cycles per second. By a Pulse is meant a change of voltage, positive or negative with respect to some reference level. Each pulse lasts two microseconds (0.000002 seconds). The standard pulse pattern is repeated every 200 microseconds. This period is the unit of time for the ENIAC, for it is the time it takes for an addition. Other operations require multiples of this period, e.g. a long multiplication takes 13 addition times.

The pulses are the money which causes the machine to be a going concern. The Cycling Unit is the mint which issues the coins, the constant transmitter a bank or clearing house. The pulses distributed to the various units stimulate the operations all round and synchronise them. When one unit has finished its work, it may transmit a pulse to another unit as an order to perform in its turn.

Each of the thirty units has more than one function. Their electrical interconnection depends on the plan of operations and is done by hand, but when once set, the machine performs extended sequences of computations automatically. Special instructions are given to each unit, but a 'Master Programmer' controls the work as a whole.

The basic unit is the *Accumulator*. An accumulator is a storing device. The chemical accumulator stores energy, the ENIAC accumulator numbers. But it also adds numbers. This it does through electrical counters. Each accumulator contains 10 decade counters and each decade counter 10 gadgets with the rather flippant-sounding name 'flip-flop'.

A flip-flop is a pair of vacuum tubes, each of which possesses three electrodes (a triode), namely (1) the Cathode which when heated, emits electrons, (2) the Anode which receives the electrons, and (3) between anode and cathode the Grid. If the voltage applied to the grid rises above a certain amount, current flows from the anode to the cathode.

Vacuum tubes of this kind often act as amplifiers, but

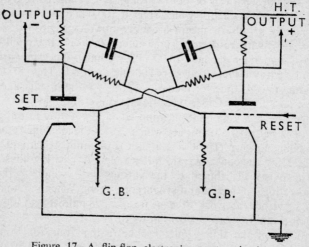

Figure 17—A flip-flop electronic counter circuit.

here they perform another service. The emission of a signal depends on whether a tube does or does not conduct, while the magnitude of the current is irrelevant. When a tube is non-conducting, there is a considerable difference of potential between anode and cathode, but when current flows through, the anode potential drops and at this moment it emits a negative signal to the outside. When its voltage rises, it emits a positive signal.

The two triodes of each flip-flop are so interconnected that never do both tubes conduct at once. A flip-flop is said to be 'on' or 'set' when its left-hand valve conducts and then only an indicating neon lamp glows. When the right-hand tube is conducting, the flip-flop is said to be 'off' or 're-set'.

The ten flip-flops within a decade counter represent from left to right the digits 0 to 9, while the whole decade represents one place of a ten-digit number. Suppose the number 6,093,528,012 were held by the accumulator, 6 would appear in the first decade counter, 0 in the second etc. The counters count electrical pulses which come, directly or indirectly, from the Cycling Unit. The 10 flip-flops within a counter ring are so connected that at any time one of them only can be 'on', and that reception of a new pulse (which alters the grid potential) causes the one flip-flop which is 'on' to be re-set and its successor to be set. This is the actual counting process. It means that the counter advances, say, from stage 4 to stage 5 and, after the next pulse received, to stage 6. Not all adding machines operate thus by actual counting. Some use addition tables.

When a counter has reached stage 9, and receives a further pulse, the last stage is re-set and the first is set, while at the same time a carry-over pulse passes to the next decade.

Subtraction is treated as a form of addition, grocer fashion. When you give your grocer a pound and your bill is 11/6, he will not say 20 minus 11/6 is 8/6, he will add on to 11/6 until he reaches 20. Here is an example of how it is done. P means plus, M minus. If 801 is to be subtracted from 527, the complement 10^{10} minus 801 is added. Thus:

$$P\ 0\ 000\ 000\ 527$$
$$M\ 9\ 999\ 999\ 199$$

$$M\ 9\ 999\ 999\ 726$$

The last line is equivalent to (−274). There is a special mechanism through which an accumulator can deliver the complement of the number which it holds.

Multiplication can be done by repeated addition, and division by repeated subtraction. But the ENIAC uses a multiplication table and has a special square-rooter and divider. Division always takes much time, but in practice it can mostly be avoided.

Each accumulator has channels for receiving and transmitting digit pulses and others for programme pulses. What it does when a programme pulse reaches it, whether it receives or transmits, whether it does so once or repeatedly, whether after transmitting a number to another unit it continues to hold it or clears it away, depends on the position of switches on the programme channel.

There are no special devices for solving algebraical and differential equations. The formulae are broken down into sequences of simple arithmetical operations, integration into step-by-step summation; the machine evaluates squares or cubes or roots and adds or subtracts the results. A group of operations may have to be repeated many times, or again the regular repetition may have to be interrupted. Sometimes the moment for a change in operations cannot be specified beforehand and the results themselves determine automatically which course the machine should follow. Indications for a new course may be a negative sign, or equality of two numbers, or a certain difference between them.

That the various units must be connected by hand, using legions of plugs and switches, is one of the drawbacks of the ENIAC. Another imperfection is its insufficient storage capacity. There are only 20 accumulators and each of them can only hold one ten-digit number. Further the ENIAC's requirements in space and electric equipment are enormous – 18,000 valves, 5,000 switches, 150 kilowatt power.

The new machines now under construction will work with one tenth of the valves and of the power and will connect the various units automatically. The EDVAC is developed in America, the A C E (mentioned in *Science News* 5) in the National Physical Laboratory in Teddington, and the EDSAC in Cambridge by the director of the Mathematical Laboratory, Dr M. V. Wilkes, who specialises in combining mathematics with electronics. The common feature of these machines is a new and surprising method of storage. A six-foot tube filled with mercury terminates at both ends in a piezo-electric quartz crystal. Such a crystal transforms pressure changes into electric impulses and vice versa (see Page 49). Thus, if signals in the form of electric waves reach the entrance quartz, it transforms them into high frequency sound waves. These travel through the mercury column and the second crystal reconverts them into electric impulses. In this form they make their way back to the first quartz and keep circling round like a moving staircase. The different rhythms or patterns of the signals represent partly instructions, partly numbers. As they leave the mercury tube, they can be selected and switched into the operating circuits so as to enter into the required operations.

Each 'memory-unit' consists of 16 tubes containing 200 lb. of mercury. Dr Wilkes plans to employ two such units with a total storage capacity of 500 ten-digit numbers. He hopes to have the machine ready for a rough testing by the end of 1948. Refinements are to be introduced later.

The new machines will use a new counting system. The fact that valves have only two positions, 'on' and 'off', has suggested the application of the binary system of notation instead of the customary decimal notation.

In the latter the symbol 1111 means $1 \times 10^3 + 1 \times 10^2 + 1 \times 10^1 + 1 \times 10^0 = 1111$. In the former the symbol 1111 means $1 \times 2^3 + 1 \times 2^2 + 1 \times 2^1 + 1 \times 2^0 = 15$; and the symbol 1010 signifies $1 \times 2^3 + 0 \times 2^2 + 1 \times 2^1 + 0 \times 2^0 = 10$.

There are no other figures but 0 and 1. A closed valve transmits no signal, an open valve one. A second signal reaching a valve necessitates carrying over as the tenth does in a decade counter. All this looks very awkward, but the system requires less complicated equipment.

A machine which can make 1 million multiplications in an hour, opens new possibilities. A scientist need no longer shrink from tackling a problem which requires several million multiplications, he need only give instructions to the machine, which will accomplish the work in a day. Quite a number of scientific domains are mentioned which baffle the physicist, not by the difficulty or profundity of the mathematical operations implied, but by the sheer amount of numerical work to be carried out and the multitude of equations to be solved.* This type of perplexity has faced scientists dealing with the structure of atoms and molecules, the movements of water and air, the results of X-ray crystallography. But the whole realm of statistics and economics, too, is waiting for the machine.

The 'Electronic Brain'

It is always much easier to introduce a false term than to evict it. The term 'electronic brain' has probably come to stay, but it must be handled with care.

Professor Hartree explains: 'The automatic control of the computing sequence by the results of the calculation itself endows the machine with "judgment" in a restricted sense, and I think it is this, or possible developments of it, which has led recently to the use of the term "electronic brain".' But it must be clearly understood that the situations requiring this judgment, the criteria to be applied, the assessment of the results of applying them and the decision on the action to be taken on the basis of this assessment, all have to be foreseen and appropriate instructions to be worked out in setting up the machine. It can only do strictly and precisely what it is told to do.

* for instance, see *Science News* 6, page 72.

'It is disconcerting how literally it takes even the most "phoney" instructions' ... It will go on for ever, say, trying to divide by zero, which no human computer would do.

Dr Wilkes observes that the ENIAC is the equivalent of a desk calculating machine plus operator, the operator being a moron who cannot think but can be trusted to do exactly as he is told.

In a letter to the *Times* (7.11.46) Professor Hartree admitted that the ENIAC exercises 'a certain amount of judgment' whereupon Sir Leon Simon asked what exactly was meant by this phrase, and suggested that Hartree's left hand had given back what his right hand had taken away. Hartree, after repeating the above quoted description, added: 'It is this faculty of selection of one procedure from several alternatives on the basis of specified criteria that is meant in writing of a machine as exercising a certain amount of judgment – a certain amount. The machine can only deal with those situations covered by the instructions supplied to it, and every step has to be foreseen and thought out by the operator and supplied to the machine as operating instructions.'

It is interesting that Babbage too ascribed judgment to his Engine. I make four objections against the phrase 'a certain amount of judgment': (1) Judgment is a faculty which one either has or has not. It is the knowledge and training that form the basis of correct judgments of which one can have a certain amount. A farmer may show excellent judgment as to crops but none as to Kant's philosophy, while a profound judge of philosophy may be unable to judge crops. Has each of them a certain amount of judgment? (2) Judgment must be conscious. If a horse finds its way to the stable while asleep, it does not exercise judgment. (3) It must be possible for a judgment to be false. The ENIAC's judgment is necessarily correct. But if it did make a mistake, whom would the engineer scold, the machine or himself? Judgment and responsibility are inseparable, even in courts of law. (4) To judge and to assess a criterion are mental faculties, and to ascribe mental faculties to a machine may appear as one step towards declaring that "man is only a machine" – quite against Professor Hartree's own intentions. Others have found it possible to describe the activities of the ENIAC without using these terms.

Sir Charles Darwin, again in that instructive *Times* correspondence, wrote: 'In popular language the word "brain" is associated with the higher realms of the intellect, but in fact a very great part of the brain is an unconscious automatic machine producing precise and sometimes very complicated reactions to stimuli. This is the only part of the brain we may aspire to imitate.'

Let us imagine some future machinery imitating in all details the activities of our brain. You may call it boldly an electronic brain, as long as you do not imagine that a brain thinks. The term 'electronic brain' is only dangerous if applied in the spirit of Karl Vogt's much-quoted dictum that the brain secretes thought as the kidney secretes urine, and if it aims at confirming that shallow creed that man is only a machine. There is no harm in using it if we realise that it is not the brain but the mind which thinks, that our mind is not the product of the brain, that generations of minds have built up the brain as generations of engineers have built the calculating machine and that the mind uses the brain as an engineer uses his calculating machine.

D. R. Hartree, *Nature*, 20th April, 1946 and 12th October, 1946; *Calculating Machines*, Inaugural Lecture, Cambridge University Press, 1947; *Journal of Scientific Instruments*, vol. 24, July, 1947; *Royal Naval Scientific Service Journal*, July, 1947; M. V. Wilkes, The ENIAC, *Electronic Engineering*, 19th April, 1947; Goldstone, *Mathematical Tables and Aids to Computation*, vol. 2, p. 97, 1946. Complete description of the ENIAC.

GLOSSARY

ANISOTROPIC crystals are crystals which have different physical properties according to the way you look at them. Thus such a crystal may show a greater resistance to the passage of an electric current when its east and west faces are connected in the circuit, than when it is turned ninety degrees and connected through its north and south. Anisotropy is a reflection of dissymmetry in the internal molecular make-up of the crystal.

BALLISTICIAN: One who studies the mathematical laws governing the aiming and firing of projectiles.

BITUMEN: crude tar.

CHEMOTHERAPY: The study of chemical substances which may be valuable in the treatment of disease.

CORONARY THROMBOSIS: The heart, like other organs, has a special supply of blood to nourish its muscle, in addition to the great mass of blood which it pumps through every minute. A coronary thrombosis is the name for the sudden clotting of the blood in one or more of the special cardiac blood vessels, the supply of nourishment to a part of the muscle being thus arrested.

ENZYME: A general term for certain protein chemicals produced by living cells and capable of bringing about various chemical reactions, though present only in traces. They are the parts of digestive juices which break up and dissolve the fat, starch and meat of food; they are also responsible for fermentation: the word 'enzyme' in fact means merely 'in yeast.'

PELLAGRA: A disease in which the chief symptoms are diarrhoea, a peculiar symmetrical dermatitis (inflammation of the skin) and often mental changes (dementia), the whole being curable by a suitable nutrition.

PHLEBITIS: Inflammation of the walls of veins, often associated with the clotting of blood in the vein, near the damage.

SACCHARIMETER: An instrument for measuring the amount of sugar in a solution, usually through the measurement of some simple physical property of sugar, such as its power to rotate the plane of polarisation of polarised light.

Our Contributors

G. W. Scott Blair was born in 1902. He is now Head of the Chemistry Department at the National Institute for Research in Dairying, but his own research is more concerned with physics than with chemistry. Previously he was at the Rothamsted Experimental Station studying the physical properties of soils, flour dough, honey and other materials connected with agriculture. In 1929-30 he held a Rockefeller Fellowship at Cornell University, where he studied the plasticity of potters' clays. He has written two books on rheology, the study of the flow and deformation of materials.

A. W. Haslett is a Cambridge graduate, who has made scientific journalism his career. He is the Editor of *Science To-day*, and author of a number of books of which *Science in Transition* has lately been recommended by the Book Society.

Gabriele Rabel, of Vienna, studied Physics and Biology at Vienna, Leipzig and Berlin. Author of various publications on the history of science including a book on *Goethe and Kant*.

D. A. Spencer is a Past President of the Royal Photographic Society (1935-36) and before the war was a Consulting Chemist and Managing Director of Colour Photographs Limited, a firm that, until the outbreak of war, supplied to British commercial photographers the majority of the colour photographs used in advertising illustrations; joined the Kodak organisation at the outbreak of war, and was loaned to the Royal Aircraft Establishment, Farnborough, subsequently becoming Principal Scientific Officer in charge of research and development on Air Photography in the Ministry of Aircraft Production. After the war, returned to the Kodak organisation, and is now Technical Adviser to the Kodak Organisation. Education: Wyggeston Grammar School, Leicester, and Royal College of Science, London.

Oliver Graham Sutton is Bashforth Professor of Mathematical Physics at the Military College of Science, Shrivenham, Wilts. He left university teaching to join the Meteorological Office in 1928. Engaged on research work on turbulence in the lower atmosphere. During the war was successively Superintendent of Research at the Chemical Warfare Experimental Station, Superintendent at the Tank Armament Research Establishment, Chief Superintendent of the Radar Research and Development Establishment, Malvern, Worcs. He is married and has two sons.

John Yudkin was born in London in 1910. He graduated in chemistry at London University in 1929 and in biochemistry at Cambridge in 1931. He spent the next twelve years at Cambridge, where he was engaged in research in biochemistry and nutrition. In his spare time, he qualified in medicine, taught physiology and was Director of Medical Studies at Christ's College. He spent three years in the R.A.M.C., part of it in West Africa, where he managed to do some further research on nutrition and also on malaria. In 1945, he was appointed to the Chair of Physiology at King's College of Household and Social Science (University of London) where he is continuing his nutritional research. His wife comes from South Africa and they have two sons.

INDEX

PENGUIN OCCASIONALS

These publications, appearing at irregular intervals, are intended for the reader desiring authoritative information on science, the arts, and contemporary affairs. Subscriptions for all of them are accepted by the publishers, Penguin Books Limited, Harmondsworth, Middlesex, at a rate of seven shillings post free for four issues of one book.

PENGUIN NEW WRITING

A collection of critical and creative writing. Its contributions are selected from the work of world-known writers, artists and new authors. Each issue contains sixteen pages of plates.

PENGUIN PARADE

Presents in an invigorating manner informative articles by authoritative writers on social and artistic affairs. The contents are varied, consisting of critical essays on the arts and social problems, short stories, poems and illustrations.

NEW BIOLOGY

A miscellany of essays summarising aspects of contemporary biological research and application. Each number has a sixteen-page inset of plates and a glossary explaining the scientific terms used in the text.

SCIENCE NEWS

Authoritative information on scientists and their work, compiled by experts for the student, teacher and the non-professional reader. Also contains line drawings and photogravure plates to illustrate the subjects treated.

PENGUIN FILM REVIEW

A publication devoted to up-to-the-minute film news and matters, surveying, in a progressive, stimulating manner, all the activities and influences of the film. Also contains thirty-two pages of illustrations from British and foreign films.

PENGUIN MUSIC MAGAZINE

Is intended to give the music lover information on the world of music and musicians. The articles, written by acknowledged authorities, are varied and controversial and each issue has thirty-two pages of illustrations.

One shilling and sixpence each